TOLD
UNDER THE
CHRISTMAS TREE

THE UMBRELLA BOOKS

TOLD UNDER THE
GREEN UMBRELLA

TOLD UNDER THE
BLUE UMBRELLA

SUNG UNDER THE
SILVER UMBRELLA

TOLD UNDER THE
MAGIC UMBRELLA

TOLD UNDER THE
STARS AND STRIPES

TOLD UNDER THE
CHRISTMAS TREE

TOLD UNDER
SPACIOUS SKIES

STORIES AND POEMS FROM
AROUND THE WORLD

TOLD
UNDER THE
CHRISTMAS TREE

*Selected by the Literature Committee of the
Association for Childhood Education International*

Illustrated by Maud and Miska Petersham

THE MACMILLAN COMPANY · NEW YORK · 1962
A Division of The Crowell-Collier Publishing Company

Ninth Printing, 1962

Library of Congress Number: 48–9525

THE MACMILLAN COMPANY, NEW YORK
BRETT-MACMILLAN LTD., GALT, ONTARIO

Printed in the United States of America

"I shall light a candle of understanding
in thine heart which shall not be put out."
—*The Apocrypha*
2 Esdras–KIV–25

A Word With the Readers

Dear boys and girls who gather about your Christmas trees to listen or to read together something significant and belonging to this festival season—I bring you a very special greeting:

First of all I wish for you that happy expectancy that comes with each new Christmas, and the opening of a new book of Christmas stories. It would be a tragic thing, indeed, if we copied each Christmas—this one exactly like the last. Your tree this year is fresh cut; it has come in all likelihood from another forest, in another part of the country. Last year, maybe from Michigan, this year from Maine. It will be lighted afresh, and I hope there will be new carols, along with the beloved and familiar ones, sung around it. This is what brings life to the keeping of an old festival, and fills it with wonder and expectancy.

This book, happily, has brought something very new and fine to your Christmas tree—it has included with the Christmas tales and legends those of the Jewish Festival of Lights. This should bring to you all a richer, more significant feeling about this winter holy-day. For it brings together other peoples and races in good fellowship. I hope when you have finished the book you will feel as I do that the Christmas tree is symbol of many things, shared throughout the world—a symbol of new life, of love, of laughter and of great rejoicing. To these the Jewish people have added one thing more in their festival. They have added *Freedom,* something, I think, the Christian world often forgets. In the story "David Comes Home" the mother reminds the children—when Anna asks who will light the first candle—that it is important —this lighting of the first of the eight festival lights— because it means not only the first light after the long darkness, but the bringing back of the light of freedom. "It means light you can put in the window without fear."

And so—while the Jewish people celebrate this birth of a new freedom, the Christian people celebrate the birth of Christ—who also brought a new freedom to the world. This is good to remember—and that each festival has been hailed with light—more light—vast light. For Hanukkah —the wonderful cruse of oil—the lighting of eight candles in memory of the eight days it burned in the holy lamp; and for Christmas the light of the Star—and the bringing it down, splitting it up, if you will, to burn in every candle flame upon the tree. And for all, Light in memory and thanksgiving inside the window of every home.

Long before Christ was born the pagan people of the world kept this season of the Winter Solstice with feasting, prayer and song. Many worshiped the sun, as the all-giving, all powerful god. When it failed them with the coming of winter, then they marked the cold and frost, killing all growing things, then they feared the sun had forsaken them. So it was natural to rejoice with the lengthening days and the waxing of the sun's power. Again, from the story "David Comes Home," David is distressed to come into a country where Christmas trees, lighted, shine everywhere. And when he says: "It makes me feel I am in the wrong place," his uncle answers him: "You don't need to feel it's strange. Many religions have a festival with lights at this time of year. Christmas trees, candles, lamps, fireworks, bonfires, they make every one long for sunlight. So when the days begin to get longer everyone celebrates."

It is good to remember that the Christmas tree is an evergreen—be it spruce or balsam or pine; that it lives in spite of cold or frost. When those first brave holy men traveled through the wilderness that covered most of Europe, to bring the good tidings of Christianity, they bore with them a small evergreen tree, and set it up among the pagan people as a symbol of everlasting life. They said in substance: "Look upon this tree. It does not cast its leaves with the weakening days of the sun. Your Frost Giants cannot kill it. It is the sign of God and Christ—all-powerful, all-loving, always with us."

I know of an old Spanish legend that tells of God, counting the seasons, and choosing winter as the darkest, coldest, most forbidding of them all, in which to send a Saviour to the world—that he might bring the promise of peace, good-will to men.

I have given you life, freedom, light as part symbol of the two festivals. And with these there is love. Love, perhaps more than all else, binds these two together. For Christians and Jews are more aware of the concern of a divine and loving father, than are other religions. Love becomes a radiant thing at Christmas time. It lies back of the choosing and giving of gifts; it lies back of the making of festival. To bring happiness to others; to call all men *brothers*. To feel for all creatures—winged and finned and footed—a cherishing tenderness, as part of the festival-spirit. This cherishing has given in story and carol a place for the ox and ass, the lamb and ewe, the cock and hen, the dog and the horse. It has imbued them with the power of speech, the power to worship and the wish to glorify. It is delightful in the story of "The Little Pagan Faun." Listen how he piped his merry tune for the Christ Child, and made him laugh when the three little seraphs had failed. In "Lullaby," it is the cat who sings the Holy Babe to sleep. And in Rachel Field's "All Through the Night" it is the creatures of the barnyard and house who take over that first Christmas and minister to the ones in the stable.

For homely, lowly love of little beast for little beast there is no story that can compare with "Dulce Domum" from Kenneth Grahame's *Wind in the Willows*. We follow the plodding of Rat and Mole through the late December night. First the "looking-in" at the human folk, snug beside their fires. We see, with them, the sleepy child being carried off to bed; we mark the loving concern of all inside for each other. Here is home! Here is the essence of what belongs to all this night. Yet Mole and Rat stand outside, lost. Mole's grieving for his own poor, little place is utterly tragic. It is Rat who comforts him—such divine compassion and understanding Rat has. Noses are pressed high into the air—all directions are sniffed for some help in finding the way home. Mole's place is found. What a feast is spread out of nothing at all. What fun Rat has in entering Mole's happy possession of what is his, so long forgotten. When the field mice come to sing outside the window their carol of "Joy in the morning," we feel, with Rat and Mole, that our cup of happiness is brimming over.

For human love, for the close-knit-tightness of love within one family circle, here is the story: "A Merry Christmas" taken from *Little Women*. Time cannot change the March family—there they are, living, taking each other and outsiders to their great heart, making so much out of so little. Here you will find the makings of a rich Christmas out of the findings of four small books, green, crimson, dove-colored and blue, under the pillows of Meg and Jo, Beth and Amy.

For the rest of the stories of Hanukkah and Christmas —they are waiting. As surely as if you held Teig's Wee Red Cap you can travel around the world—to Jerusalem, Bethlehem, the Tyrol, the Balkans, to Provence, the Gaspé. You can stand beside Dobry, in the cold and snow of just before Christmas, and watch him carve with love and adoration the figures of Mary, Joseph and the Child. Here is wonder and that abounding delight in finding something that truly belongs to this time of festival.

And let us not forget laughter. Where love is there must always be laughter. It springs forth as naturally as gay flowers in a well-tended garden. For good, bubbling laughter, for rib-tickling absurdities, here is "The Peterkins' Christmas Tree." Choose it for the time when the fire burns low, the presents are all opened and bed-time is not far off.

One last thing I would have you remember. Whatever young people and adults bring to their Festival of Lights and Christmas—that—and that alone—will they find there. If these stand only for the giving of material gifts, done up in bright ribbon, then they will be lost before the New Year comes in. But—if they stand for a rebirth of faith and freedom—for a lighting-up time of hearts as well as candles, lamps and fires; if they stand for love between all peoples, and for laughter, together, and rejoicing—then all who gather around the Christmas tree or beside the eight-branch candlesticks, will find something that kindles the spirit and makes of the world an abiding place of peace and good-will.

It is not the small differences between races and creeds that matter! What matters is the sharing of all the best that Christmas and Hanukkah hold and the wish to come together in good fellowship—one group with another. Your Christmas tree can be a poverty tree, your Menorah, and every lighted candle can be a poor symbol, neither reaching farther than your four walls, or they can be symbols of eternal light, eternal life, reaching into the far corners of the world.

In presenting these stories the editors have not been so concerned about the sources of festival as with its inner meaning. This year we need to flood the world with the blessedness of Christmas, the burning freedom of Hanukkah. The world needs the gifts of laughter and deep, abiding love. So we wish all who gather beside their Christmas tree—we wish you, every one—a merry and a blessed holy-tide.

——*Ruth Sawyer*

Contents

CONTENTS

"KINDLE THE TAPER LIKE THE STEADFAST STAR"

"THIS IS THE WEEK WHEN CHRISTMAS COMES"

Words from an Old Spanish Carol

Shall I tell you who will come
   To Bethlehem on Christmas morn?
Who will kneel them gently down
   Before the Lord new-born?

One small fish from the river,
   With scales of red, red gold,
One wild bee from the heather,
   One grey lamb from the fold,
One ox from the high pasture,
   One black bull from the herd,
One goatling from the far hills,
   One white, white bird.

And many children—God give them grace,
   Bringing tall candles to light Mary's face.

Shall I tell you who will come
   To Bethlehem on Christmas morn?
Who will kneel them gently down
   Before the Lord new-born?

                  ——*Ruth Sawyer*

"Words from an Old Spanish Carol" is from *The Long Christmas,* by Ruth Sawyer; copyright, 1941, by Ruth Sawyer; this selection reprinted by permission of the Viking Press, Inc., New York.

Lullaby

A LONG, long time ago, the little Christ-child was born in a far away country, in a stable among the animals.

There were His Mother and Saint Joseph as well as a good ox, a gentle ass and the other beasts who watched over the Christ-child.

When the news of His birth spread, everyone hurried to the stable to pay Him homage. There were kings, and shepherds and just simple townfolk.

When the children of the village learned the good news, they too wanted to welcome the little Baby and to bring Him gifts.

It was a clear Christmas night, and so the children followed the little bright star in the skies until it led them to the stable where the Christ-child was lying in His manger.

And oh what a crowd came to the stable to greet the Christ-child!

4

And what gifts they brought with them!

There was the Kubus boy, who brought a big, black cock. And a very proud strutter he was!

"Cock-a-doodle-doo!" he cried in greeting.

And here was the little Hanka girl with a cake of fresh cheese for the Christ-child.

The little Franus boy came, dragging his goat on a rope.

And right in front was Basia, the goose-girl, with a big, fat goose under her arm.

Behind the children you could see the Kujawiak couple, the newlyweds, with the whole jolly wedding party from Krakow, even the musicians.

The Child listened with great joy to the music and singing. He watched the merry people dancing and although it was growing quite late, He was wide awake and playful.

His Mother knew it was time for the little One to go to sleep. The shepherds saw her worried face, and gently urged the visitors to go.

They slipped away in twos and threes. Out through the stable-door they went, first the simple townfolk, then the villagers, then the wise men, and finally the children and the dancers.

Now the little Christ-child was alone with His Mother and Saint Joseph and the animals.

His Mother began to sing a lullaby. Hum ... Hum ... she crooned, yet it sounded very high. The Baby would not close His eyes or fall asleep.

Next, Saint Joseph took his turn at humming a song; but His voice was deep and loud. He only made the Baby open His eyes wider than ever.

It was really late now, nearly midnight. But His Mother had a wise thought. She asked the animals to help Her.

"Will you, good ox, or you gentle ass sing my Baby to sleep?"

"Yes indeed," said the good ox.

"Gladly," said the gentle ass.

"Moo-OO!" went the ox; stretching his great neck.

"Haw-ee, haw-ee!" brayed the ass.

The poor little Child was only frightened the more.

"What shall we do?" cried His Mother. She was at her wit's end.

Just then she saw a tiny tiger-cat, curled up like a snail, in a far corner of the stable.

"Come kitty, kitty-kitty," she called. "Come little Purry-whiskers and put my Baby to sleep."

Little Purry-whiskers lifted his head. He looked at his sooty coat and was very much ashamed. You see, he had been sleeping in the ashes on top of his mistress' stove. When he had heard the crowds on their way to the stable, he had left his warm home and followed them. He had come with the villagers, the wise men, the children, and the dancers.

And now they had left him behind in the stable.

His white chin was covered with soot. And so was each one of his four paws. Even the tip of his tail was dusty with ashes.

"Oh Purry-whiskers!" thought he. "How can you show your sooty self, shame on you!"

And he began to wash. How he licked himself! First he started with his dusty chin. . . .

"Kitty, kitty, come to me," the Child's Mother coaxed.

He washed his face very carefully and then he began on the little white patch behind his ear.

"Please hurry," Saint Joseph called. But the kitten just went on licking and licking. He had nearly finished his last hind paw.

Even the good ox lost patience.

"Won't you ever finish?" he mooed.

But Purry-whiskers was cleaning the last bit of ash from the tip of his tail. Now he was ready. He softly pattered to the manger. Up he hopped. He curled himself at the Christ-child's feet and then he began to purr.

And what he purred was his own lullaby, the lullaby that every kitten knows.

Ah,—Ah, Pussies gay, One wears stripes, and one is gray
One is Short, The other tall, And I love them, Big or small.
Mew—Mew, Pussy do; One white mitten, one white shoe
Though you're small and even fat, you are still my pussy-
cat!

. . . but the Christ-child had fallen sound asleep.

Ever after that night the Purry-whiskers made sure never to be caught again with a smudgy face.

And that is why you see him washing himself so often.

——*Josephine B. Bernhard*

Long, Long Ago

Wind through the olive trees
   Softly did blow,
Round little Bethlehem
   Long, long ago.

Sheep on the hillside lay
   Whiter than snow.
Shepherds were watching them
   Long, long ago.

Then from the happy sky
   Angels bent low,
Singing their songs of joy
   Long, long ago.

For in a manger bed
   Cradled we know.
Christ came to Bethlehem
   Long, long ago.
       ——*Anonymous*

All Through the Night

ALL THAT DAY the Inn Yard had been thronged with people coming to pay their taxes in the town of Bethlehem. The small sturdy watchdog who slept in the stable and picked up what food he could find had never before seen such a crowd of travelers.

When night fell he was tired from barking at so many strangers and their beasts, and with scurrying out of the way of feet and hoofs. But for all the barking and running about it had been a good day. The Inn had overflowed into the yard. There had been a fire there with meat roasting over it and pots that sent out clouds of savory steam. Many a rich morsel had fallen his way, so he felt well content as he crept into his corner of the stable near the oxen's stall.

He and they greeted each other and exchanged news of the day.

"Yes, we, too, have been busy," the oxen told him.

"Heavy loads for us since daybreak and the roads round Bethlehem so choked with carts and caravans and herds and flocks we could hardly move sometimes."

"And rude, stupid creatures they were to meet!" the ass put in from her corner. "With no manners at all or sense enough to follow their own noses. Some even dared to dispute the right of way with me, but I held my ground."

"I have no doubt you did," said the dog, for he knew the ass was not one to be persuaded against her will. He turned himself round and round in a pile of straw to make himself comfortable and fell to licking a bruised spot on his leg.

"There must have been many sheep," the old ewe joined in from her pen. "I could not see them because I was shut in here with my two lambs, but I could tell by their voices that some came from places farther away than Judea. I should have liked to see them."

"Well," the dog told her, "I found them a dusty, frightened lot. I was thankful not to have their herding in my charge. And the goats were no better," he added, that the bearded gray goat might be sure to hear. He and the goat were not upon friendly terms and took pleasure in tormenting each other.

"Peace and quiet. Peace and quiet at last," the doves cooed from the rafters. "Peace and quiet till morning, that is all we ask."

The hens made soft clucking sounds to show that they were in complete agreement.

But the cock with his scarlet comb and burnished tail feathers, stepping about in search of stray kernels, was of a different mind. "I like noise and bustle myself." He voiced his opinion loudly. "Peace is all very well for those who haven't the spirit for something better. Now *I* can hardly wait for morning."

"Everyone to his own taste," the mild-eyed cow put in her word, shifting her cud deftly and flicking her tail as she did so. "If it were always day or always night we should not all be satisfied."

"Well said. Well said," the doves agreed in drowsy unison from the dimness of the eaves.

Darkness gathered there first. The swallows were already seeking their nests, while the bats were beginning to stretch and unfold their lean, black wings.

Night was coming fast and all the birds and beasts and insects of the stable knew that it belonged to them. The world was theirs as the world of day could never be. When the sun rose man would be their master again. They would carry his burdens or feed or serve him according to their different gifts. But night was their own, when they might move or fight or take counsel together without man's interference. It was good that this should be so, the little dog thought, as he burrowed deeper into the straw.

His sworn enemy the cat slid by. She moved like a shadow with fiery-green eyes ready to pounce upon the mice who were already squeaking and scampering at their play. But the dog was too tired and comfortable to give chase, so for once he let her pass unmolested. All about him crickets chirped in rusty chorus and sometimes a bat swooped so low he could feel the stir of its wings. The darkness was warm and alive with the familiar scents of fur and feathers and grain and straw.

"Rest well. Rest well. Rest well." The doves cooed sleepily, making a soft sound in their throats that was like the bubbling of a well-filled pot over a fire.

Night had come to Bethlehem. The Inn had been full hours ago. The dog could hear late travelers being turned away. The stable door was securely bolted against intruders and the wind was rising, frosty and keen. Through an opening in the roof a star shone bright as purest silver.

"I never saw a star look so large or so near," the cock observed as he moved about with his spurred, high-stepping walk. "Somehow it makes me very restless, and there is something strange in the air. Perhaps you have felt it, too?"

But the dog made no answer. He yawned and laid his pointed muzzle on his paws and prepared himself for sleep.

He woke at the sound of voices outside and roused himself to bark. But though the hair rose along his back, no sound came rumbling from his throat. The bolt was drawn and the stable door opened to lantern light and the dim shapes of two men and a donkey on whose back a woman sat, wrapped in a heavy cloak.

"Well"—the voice of the Inn Keeper sounded short and impatient—"if you cannot go on, there is only the stable to offer. Coming as you have at such an hour, you are fortunate to have this shelter till morning."

"The roads were crowded," the Man answered him, "and our pace was slow because of my wife. You can see that she is nearly spent."

"Yes, yes." The Inn Keeper was already shutting the door. "I am sorry for your plight, but I tell you there is no room left."

The dog was on his feet. He could hear the other animals rising about him, yet not one of them uttered a sound. Their throats were as silent as his own.

In the flickering lantern light he watched the Man lift the Woman from the donkey's back and set her upon her feet. She was so weary she would have fallen but for the Man's arms.

"Joseph," she said, "you must not be troubled for me, even if it should be that the time has come." . . . She rested her head on the Man's shoulder and sighed so softly it might have been one of the doves in the rafters drawing closer to her mate.

"But, Mary," the Man went on, "it is not right and fitting that it should be here,—not in a stable among the beasts."

"Who knows," she comforted him, "what is to be? These beasts are more kind than men who kill and hurt one another. I am glad to be here. Their warm breath comforts me. Their straw is clean and soft to rest upon."

Everywhere beyond the ring of light that the lantern made, bright eyes were upon the strangers. Furry ears and quivering noses pointed, alert and watchful.

The strange donkey, freed of his load, found a place beside the ass. He sank down, too tired to drink water from the trough or reach for a mouthful of hay.

A hush was on the stable. Not only were all throats silent, but no wings stirred; no claws scratched and not a hoof pounded. And in that hour nothing died. The young swallows and mice were safe from their enemies, for a mystery greater than death held them all in its power.

The lantern flickered and went out.

"Our oil is gone!" the Man cried out in distress.

"There will be light enough." The Woman spoke in a faint voice, and as if in answer the star in the roof gap shone brighter than before.

How long it was after that the little dog could not tell. Morning was still far off, yet the cock suddenly lifted up his voice, so shrill and clear it seemed he would split himself in two. It was not like any other cockcrow since the world began and it rose higher than the rafters and mounted to heaven itself. At the same instant each creature found voice and joined with him. Every living thing in the stable had a part in that swelling chorus of praise. Even the bees hummed till their hive throbbed with music, sweeter than all its store of honey.

"What manner of place is this?" the Man cried out. "What beasts are these who have the tongues of angels?"

But the Woman answered him softly out of the shadows. "It was they who gave us shelter this night. Let them draw near and be the first to worship."

She drew aside the folds of her cloak and light filled the stable even to the farthest corners. The dog cowered before such strange brightness. When he dared to look more closely he saw that it encircled the head of an infant, new born.

"There is no bed for him to lie upon," the Man sighed. "Only this"—and he pointed to the manger.

"Bring it here," the Mother said. "My heart tells me there will be nights when he will have no place at all to rest his head."

So the Child lay quiet in the straw-filled wooden manger and all the animals came to view him there—the oxen, the cow, the ass and the donkey, the ewe and her lambs, the gray goat, the dog, the hens and the proud cock ruffling his feathers. The cat left off her prowling to join them and the mice ran beside her without fear. The crickets came, too, drawn from the comfort of their warm straw; the bees, from their snug hive. The tireless ants and spiders left their toil to draw near. The swallows in the eaves flew down; the bats bent low on their dark wings, and the doves came closest of all with their soft murmurs above the manger. When they had all seen the Wonder they returned to their places and were quiet again.

All but the dog. He could not rest as he had before. He stretched himself beside the manger and lay with his head on his folded paws, his eyes wide and watchful as the hours passed.

Long before sunrise the door opened without sound of bolt being drawn and a band of Shepherds came in. They bore a strange tale on their lips and they also worshiped on bended knees. One carried a lamb in his arms and the Child answered its bleating with a smile.

"Behold the Lamb of God," they said one to another as they turned to go back to their flocks on the hills.

The star grew pale and through the gap in the stable roof morning showed rosy in the east. Even before the cock hailed it, the dog knew that the sun was up. But he did not move lest he rouse the three in his care. It was then that he saw a strange thing.

The rafters high above cast their shadows as the rising sun struck through. Two of the beams crossed in sharp black bars that fell directly across the sleeping Child. The little dog could not tell why the sight should make him cower in sudden fear.

Then the cock crowed three times and the first sounds of people stirring in the Inn and yard began.

He watched the Man and the Woman preparing to go. He saw the donkey being watered and fed and the blanket fitted in place. He saw the Mother wrap her Son warmly against the cold before the Man set them upon the donkey's back and lifted a heavy bundle on his own.

"Come," he said and opened the stable door. "We must make haste."

Stiff from his long vigil, the dog rose and followed them to the door. He watched them cross the Inn yard in the early light and join other travelers who were already thronging the roads leading to and from Bethlehem. Soon they would be lost to his sight, those Three whom he had guarded through the hours of darkness.

"Ah," cried the cock, preening his burnished feathers, "what a morning!" He strutted over to where bits of food and grain lay scattered and began to forage for stray morsels.

The dog lifted his head and sniffed hungrily. He could tell that pots were already on the fires. The sharp morning air brought the savory news to him and he knew that by keeping close to the kitchen he would soon be well filled. He remembered a bone he had buried yesterday in a secluded spot. Yet he did not seek it. He trotted past the kitchen doors, and though his nose twitched at the smells that he was leaving he kept it pointed straight ahead.

"Wait. Wait." His bark rang out sharp and determined and his paws clicked over the stones as he ran.

He did not pause till he had caught up with the Man who led the plodding donkey and his burden along the dusty road.

"Here I am!" He barked again as he fell into step beside them ."Let me come with you."

——*Rachel Field*

The Friendly Beasts

Jesus our brother, strong and good,
Was humbly born in a stable rude,
And the friendly beasts around Him stood,
Jesus our brother, strong and good.

"I," said the donkey shaggy and brown,
"I carried His mother up hill and down,
I carried her safely to Bethlehem town;
I," said the donkey, shaggy and brown.

"I," said the cow all white and red,
"I gave Him my manger for His bed,
I gave Him my hay to pillow His head;
I," said the cow all white and red.

"I," said the sheep with curly horn,
"I gave Him my wool for His blanket warm,
He wore my coat on Christmas morn;
I." said the sheep with curly horn.

"I," said the dove, from the rafters high,
"Cooed Him to sleep, my mate and I,
We cooed Him to sleep, my mate and I;
I," said the dove, from the rafters high.

And every beast, by some good spell,
In the stable dark was glad to tell,
Of the gift he gave Immanuel,
The gift he gave Immanuel.

——Twelfth-Century Carol

Once in the Year

WHEN SUPPER WAS OVER, Martha and Andrew
put on their warm coats. Andrew pulled his cap down over
his ears and Martha threw a woolen shawl over her head
and tied it under her chin. Laughter was in their voices and
lightness in their movements, for this was one time when
care could be set aside. The animals had been fed early
and bedded down for the night so that Andrew had no
worries for them; and Martha had spent the whole week
cooking and cleaning so her mind was free from household chores. Her husband and her son, and Benj who
had been part of the farm for so many years, would not
want for anything that was hers to give them for days
to come.

"You'll be asleep when we get back," Andrew said, just
as they were going out the door, "so the next greeting
we'll be giving you will be Merry Christmas."

Once in the Year, bv Elizabeth Yates; copyright, 1947, by Elizabeth Yates
McGreal; this selection reprinted by permission of Coward-McCann, Inc.

Martha's eyes twinkled. Even the plain words said every night of the year, "Good-night, Peter," seemed so much more meaningful when the next ones would be "Merry Christmas!"

Then they called good-by and stepped out into the frosty night.

Peter ran to the window and pushed the curtain aside to watch them. Arm in arm they went over the path, two black figures on the white field of snow, with stars looking down on them and the dark lines of the hills rimming them in a known world. Now they were running a little, then they stopped as if to catch their breath and Peter saw his mother toss her head quickly, then his father threw back his head and laughed.

What a wonderful time Christmas Eve was, Peter thought, the world so still and everyone in it so happy. For so many days of the year his father was serious and full of care and his mother's thoughts seemed far ahead of her as if she were thinking of all the things she had to do; but tonight they were gay and light-hearted.

When Peter could see them no longer, he returned to the circle of warmth by the stove. Benj was sitting there, gazing dreamily into the coals. Peter brought up a stool and sat beside him. It might be beautiful outside and great things might be going on in the village, but here it was warm and the deep wonder of the night was as much within the familiar kitchen as it was outdoors in the starlit quiet.

"Tell me a story, Benj. Tell me about Christmas, how it all happened," Peter said.

Peter knew it well but he wanted to hear it again, and

though the story itself did not change, Benj never failed to add something new at the end.

Benj nodded slowly and began to tell Peter the old story of the stable at Bethlehem, of the man and woman who had found shelter there because there was no room at the inn, and of the ox and the ass who had moved aside a little to share their place with the travelers.

"And out on the hillside there were shepherds with their sheep," Benj went on, "some of them talking around a bit of a fire they had made, holding out their hands to warm them for there was a chill on the air that night; and some of them had gone to sleep. But, of a sudden, the night about them became white with light. They looked up to see where the light came from and it was as if the very doors of heaven had opened to them. Then they heard an angel telling them what had happened."

"What had happened, Benj? What made the night turn to light?"

"In that stable yonder in Bethlehem a child had been born to the woman. He it was that the ages had been waiting for. He it was who would bring true light to the world, and though he would not do it as a child, nor yet as a young man, and though the world would stumble on in its darkness for many years until he came to the fullness of his manhood, there was light that night of his birth. A kind of sign it was of what his coming into the world meant, and the darkness would never be so dark again."

Benj was seeing it all, as clearly as had the shepherds on that far away hillside, and his eyes were shining.

"The shepherds left their flocks in charge of their dogs and went to the stable to see the child. A fine strong boy he was. They brought food in their pouches to share with the man and the woman, and when they returned to the hillside they were not hungry, for the joy they bore with them fed them as heartily as the bread and the cheese they had left behind. After a while the night grew quiet again. Midnight came. The family were alone in the stable. And then—" Benj breathed deeply, as if recalling something so marvelous that there might not be words to tell of it, "a wonderful thing happened."

"What was it, Benj?" Peter asked. The story had been familiar to him up to this point but now it was new.

"In that dark stillness, unbroken by even a baby's crying, the creatures in the stable began to talk among themselves—the great slow-moving ox, and the tired little ass, a half-grown sheep that had followed the shepherds to Bethlehem, and a brown hen who had roosted in the rafters at sundown. They talked together and to the child."

"Didn't they talk to the others—the man and the woman?"

Benj shook his head. "Those two had gone to sleep." He looked at Peter and spoke slowly. "It's said that on every Christmas Eve, near midnight and for a while after, the creatures talk among themselves. It is the only time they do so, the only time of all the year."

"Can anyone hear them, Benj?"

The old man shook his head again. "Only the still of heart, for only they will listen long enough to catch the meaning of so strange a sound."

"Have you heard them, Benj?"

"I have, Peter, times without number, and they always say the same thing."

"What do they say?"

"I cannot tell you now. What they say to me might be very different from what they would say to anyone else."

Peter looked at the clock. The hands were at nine. Such a long way it was to midnight, yet he knew that somehow he must stay awake to hear the creatures talk together.

A while later Benj banked the stove, lowered the lamp and said good-night to Peter. Peter went upstairs to bed and Benj went out to the barn to make his nightly rounds. The animals were safe and contented, he knew, but this was one night when he must be doubly sure, tired though his limbs might be from the work of the day.

The quietness of night enveloped the farmhouse, enveloped the world; but the night was unlike any other, for wonder was abroad and there was an air of expectancy that beggared sleep.

Up in his room, Peter heard the clock strike eleven, then he heard the laughter of his mother and the well-known tones of his father's voice as they came up the path from the village. Their voices lowered as they entered the house and talked together in the kitchen, warming their hands by the stove. Quietly they came up the stairs and stood outside Peter's door, then the door was pushed open a crack.

"He's asleep," Andrew said.

"Good, then we haven't wakened him," Martha added. She would have liked to cross the room and tuck his covers in, but she would not risk waking him at such an hour and the next day Christmas.

Peter lay very still, his eyelids trembling as he kept them closed over his eyes. What would his mother say if she came over to the bed and saw that he had not undressed—that he had put a stone under his pillow so discomfort would keep him awake? The door closed and his parents tiptoed into their own room. There were small sounds and whispers, a bit of soft laughter, then stillness and the ticking of the kitchen clock telling Peter that its hands were drawing near midnight.

Slowly, one foot then another, he got out of bed and put on his coat that had been made from the wool of Biddy's last shearing. He took his shoes in his hands and crept down the stairs to the kitchen. Peering up into the face of the clock he saw the hands at a quarter to twelve. He sat down on the floor to put on his shoes. Going to the door he opened it noiselessly and closed it behind him, then ran lightly to the barn.

It was very still in the barn and very dark, but as his eyes became used to the darkness he could discern dimly the familiar shapes of the farm animals in their chosen positions of sleep. The barn seemed strange so near the mid hour of night and Peter, to assure himself, went to each animal in turn, to caress them and feel the comfort of their knowing presences.

First, there was the black yearling. Biddy's last lamb who was growing to be the flock's leader. Peter slipped into the pen where the sheep were folded and whistled softly. The yearling shook itself out of sleep and came over to the boy, rubbing against him and eating the raw potato Peter had brought in his pocket.

Then Peter went to the stall where his father's work horse stood. The horse whinnied and reached for the lump of sugar Peter offered.

Then he went to the stanchions where the cows were, all three of them lying with their legs tucked under them and chewing their cuds peacefully. Peter stroked each gentle head and took the rhythmic sound of chewing as their sufficient greeting.

Going over to the corner where the hens roosted for the night, he looked up at them.

"Hello," he said. "It's just Peter. Don't be alarmed."

They moved on their perch ever so lightly and started talking among themselves, soft sounds as if they were so far asleep they could not bear to be wakened but still must let Peter know that they were aware of his presence and were glad for it.

Peter found a pile of hay near the horse's stall and curled up in it to listen to the creatures when midnight came. He was hardly settled when from far down in the valley the village clock could be heard. Peter held his breath as twelve strokes resounded on the night with slow and measured import. While their echo faded, the same stillness filled the barn that had been there when Peter first entered; but it was only for a moment. Soon it was broken by a rustle of straw here, and a stamp of a hoof there, a single deep-toned baa-aa, a short neigh, and chickens cooing in their sleep.

Almost before Peter realized what had happened, he was caught up in a conversation the creatures were having. It was an old story they were telling, as far as he could make out, one the horse had heard as a colt from his dam, and long before that it had first been told by a small weary ass. It was a story the cow had heard as a calf and which had been first told by an ox in a stable in Judea. It was a story that the sheep knew because all sheep heard it from their ewes when they were lambs. It was a story that a single brown hen had left as a heritage for all hens. And they told it again, each in a way peculiar to cow, horse, sheep, hen, as if to remind themselves of why this night was hallowed.

"I had worked all day," the cow said, thinking for that moment that she was the ox and might speak as such. "I had drawn heavy loads and knocked my feet against the rough stones in the fields, but when the child was born and all that light shone in my stable the work I had done seemed a beautiful thing and the thought of it no longer tired me. It was the light that made me see we were born to serve so One on high might rule."

"Oh, I was weary, too," the horse said, and his voice became small and plaintive as he fancied himself the ass. "We had journeyed so far that day, so very far, and mind you, as it turned out, it was two I had been carrying, not just one. My head drooped so low that I thought I could never lift it again and even the hay in the manger did not interest me. Then came that light and everything was different. I felt so humble in its glow that I did not care if I never raised my head again. And I was glad my back was strong to bear burdens and that my feet could be sure, no matter how rough the way. I was glad, too, that man had use for me, for serving him brought me closer to the God he serves."

"I was not weary or burdened," the black yearling spoke up, thinking he was the half-grown lamb that had followed in the wake of the shepherds. "I had been grazing all day and when darkness came and the flock had been folded I had tucked my legs under me to sleep. Then the light appeared. It was such a dazzling thing it took away from me all thinking. There were no thoughts in my head, such as 'Shall I stay? Shall I go?' There was only one compelling desire and it drew me to the stable where I stayed. I saw my shepherd giving his pouch of food to the mother and I thought then, 'Take what I have and use it, it is all for glory.'"

One of the hens shook her feathers and came down from the roost. The sound of her voice was sweetly melodious, as if the feathered creatures of the world in making her their spokesman had loaned her the gift of song.

"I said to myself, 'This is a very great moment. How shall I praise God for letting me be here?' There was only one thing to do. I nestled down in the straw and laid an egg so when it came time for the night's fast to be broken there would be something for hungry folk to eat. And so, ever since that time long ago, an egg has been our way of praise. It is our highest gift."

The rustling in the straw ceased. The hen's slow sleepy movements on the roost were over. Not so much as the stamp of a hoof or the muffled baa-ing of a sheep broke the stillness in the barn. Peter rubbed his eyes in astonishment. He had heard the creatures talking on Christmas Eve, talking of what had taken place on the first Christmas Eve.

He knew something now of what dwelt behind the quietness in the soft eyes of horse and cow, the gentle gaze of the sheep, and the cool glance of the hen. They had never forgotten the time when they had been of use, and remembering it had marked their lives with blessing. Like a shining thread running down the ages, it gave meaning and dignity to the work each one did. Love had made them wise that night, lightening every labor they might do thereafter.

There was a stir among the dark shadows of the barn and Peter saw old Benj coming to stand beside him. It was too dark to see his face, but his form and his foot-steps were unmistakable. Peter had thought he was alone in the barn, but it did not surprise him to know that Benj had been there, too.

"I heard them talking together," Peter whispered ex-citedly. "Did you hear them, Benj—"

"Aye, I heard them," the old man nodded.

"It was wonderful what they said, wasn't it, Benj?"

"Wonderful, indeed."

Peter took Benj's hand and the two started back to the house across the white barnyard under the star-decked sky.

"It's the same for us as it is for them, isn't it, Benj?"

"Aye, it's the same for us as we all serve the one Father, but only the still of heart can catch that message and link it to their lives."

A few minutes later Peter was ready to close his eyes in sleep, when he smiled to himself in the darkness of his room. Christmas seemed a more beautiful time than it had ever seemed before—a time when one gave of one's best and rejoiced in the giving because it was one's all.

And then, it was almost as if his mother were standing beside his bed for he could hear her talking to him; but it was not her words, it was the words her mother had used when Martha was a little girl.

"When something wonderful happens to people on Christmas Eve, it is to be cherished in the heart and in the mind. We must not be afraid of the wonderful things, nor must we let others laugh them away from us. Only thus do we learn to hold our dreams—"

Peter smiled to himself again, then he turned his head on his pillow and went to sleep.

——*Elizabeth Yates*

Shall I to the Byre Go Down

Shall I to the byre go down
    Where the stalled oxen are?
Or shall I climb the mountain's crown
    To see the rising star?
Or shall I walk the golden floor
    Where the King's feast is spread?
Or shall I seek the poor man's door
    And ask to break his bread?

It matters not. Go where you will,
    Kneel down in cattle stall,
Climb up the cold and starlit hill,
    Enter in hut or hall,
To the warm fireside give your cheek,
    Or turn it to the snow,
It matters not; the One you seek
    You'll find where'er you go.

His sandal-sole is on the earth,
    His head is in the sky,
His voice is in the baby's mirth
    And in the old man's sigh,
His shadow falls across the sea,
    His breath is in the wind,
His tears with all who grieve left He,
    His heart with all who sinned.

"Shall I to the Byre Go Down" is from *Come Christmas,* by Eleanor Farjeon; copyright, 1927, by J. B. Lippincott Company; reprinted by permission.

Whether you share the poor man's mite
Or taste the King's own fare,
He whom you go to seek tonight
Will meet you everywhere;
For He is where the cattle wend,
And where the planets shine—
Lo, He is in your eyes! Oh friend,
Stand still and look in mine.

———*Eleanor Farjeon*

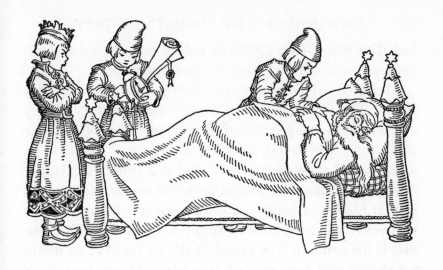

In the Great Walled Country

AWAY AT THE NORTHERN end of the world, farther than men have ever gone with their ships or their sleds, and where most people suppose that there is nothing but ice and snow, is a land full of children, called The Great Walled Country. This name is given because all around the country is a great wall, hundreds of feet thick and hundreds of feet high. It is made of ice, and never melts, winter or summer; and of course it is for this reason that more people have not discovered the place.

The land, as I said, is filled with children, for nobody who lives there ever grows up. The king and the queen, the princes and the courtiers, may be as old as you please, but they are children for all that. They play a great deal of the time with dolls and tin soldiers, and every night at seven o'clock have a bowl of bread and milk and go to

"In the Great Walled Country" is from *Why the Chimes Rang and Other Stories,* by Raymond MacDonald Alden; copyright, 1906, 1934, by Raymond MacDonald Alden; this selection reprinted by permission of The Bobbs-Merrill Company.

bed. But they make excellent rulers, and the other children are well pleased with the government.

There are all sorts of curious things about the way they live in The Great Walled Country, but this story is only of their Christmas season. One can imagine what a fine thing their Christmas must be, so near the North Pole, with ice and snow everywhere; but this is not all. Grandfather Christmas lives just on the north side of the country, so that his house leans against the great wall and would tip over if it were not for its support. Grandfather Christmas is his name in The Great Walled Country; no doubt we should call him Santa Claus here. At any rate, he is the same person, and, best of all the children in the world, he loves the children behind the great wall of ice.

One very pleasant thing about having Grandfather Christmas for a neighbor is that in The Great Walled Country they never have to buy their Christmas presents. Every year, on the day before Christmas, before he makes up his bundles for the rest of the world, Grandfather Christmas goes into a great forest of Christmas trees that grows just back of the palace of the king of The Great Walled Country, and fills the trees with candy and books and toys and all sorts of good things. So when night comes, all the children wrap up snugly, while the children in all other lands are waiting in their beds, and go to the forest to gather gifts for their friends. Each one goes by himself so that none of his friends can see what he has gathered; and no one ever thinks of such a thing as taking a present for himself. The forest is so big that there is room for everyone to wander about without meeting the people from whom he has secrets, and there are always enough nice things to go around.

So Christmas time is a great holiday in that land, as it is in all best places in the world. They have been celebrating it in this way for hundreds of years, and since Grandfather Christmas does not seem to grow old any faster than the children, they will probably do so for hundreds of years to come.

But there was once a time, so many years ago that they would have forgotten all about it if the story were not written in their Big Book and read to them every year, when the children in The Great Walled Country had a very strange Christmas. There came a visitor to the land. He was an old man, and was the first stranger for very many years who had succeeded in getting over the wall. He looked so wise, and was so much interested in what he saw and heard, that the king invited him to the palace, and he was treated with every possible honor.

When this old man had inquired about their Christmas celebration, and was told how they carried it on every year, he listened gravely, and then, looking wiser than ever, he said to the king:

"That is all very well, but I should think that children who have Grandfather Christmas for a neighbor could find a better and easier way. You tell me that you all go out on Christmas Eve to gather presents to give to one another the next morning. Why take so much trouble, and act in such a roundabout way? Why not go out together, and everyone get his own presents? That would save the trouble of dividing them again, and everyone would be better satisfied, for he could pick out just what he wanted for himself. No one can tell what you want as well as you can."

This seemed to the king a very wise saying, and he called

all his courtiers and counselors about him to hear it. The wise stranger talked further about his plan, and when he had finished they all agreed that they had been very foolish never to have thought of this simple way of getting their Christmas gifts.

"If we do this," they said, "no one can ever complain of what he has, or wish that someone had taken more pains to find what he wanted. We will make a proclamation, and always after this follow the new plan."

So the proclamation was made, and the plan seemed as wise to the children of the country as it had to the king and the counselors. Everyone had at some time been a little disappointed with his Christmas gifts; now there would be no danger of that.

On Christmas Eve they always had a meeting at the palace, and sang carols until the time for going to the forest. When the clock struck ten everyone said, "I wish you a Merry Christmas!" to the person nearest him, and then they separated to go their ways to the forest. On this particular night it seemed to the king that the music was not quite so merry as usual, and that when the children spoke to one another their eyes did not shine as gladly as he had noticed them in other years; but there could be no good reason for this, since everyone was expecting a better time than usual. So he thought no more of it.

There was only one person at the palace that night who was not pleased with the new proclamation about the Christmas gifts. This was a little boy named Inge, who lived not far from the palace with his sister. Now his sister was a cripple, and had to sit all day looking out of the window from her chair; and Inge took care of her, and tried to make her life happy from morning till night. He had always gone to the forest on Christmas Eve and returned with his arms and pockets loaded with pretty things for his sister, which would keep her amused all the coming year. And although she was not able to go after presents for her brother, he did not mind that at all, especially as he had other friends who never forgot to divide their good things with him.

But now, said Inge to himself, what would his sister do? For the king had ordered that no one should gather any presents except for himself, or any more than he could carry away at once. All of Inge's friends were busy planning what they would pick for themselves, but the poor crippled child could not go a step toward the forest. After thinking about it a long time, Inge decided that it would not be wrong if, instead of taking gifts for himself, he took them altogether for his sister. This he would be very glad to do; for what did a boy who could run about and play in the snow care for presents, compared with a little girl who could only sit still and watch others having a good time? Inge did not ask the advice of anyone, for he was a little afraid others would tell him he must not do it; but he silently made up his mind not to obey the proclamation.

And now the chimes had struck ten, and the children were making their way toward the forest in starlight that was so bright that it almost showed their shadows on the sparkling snow. As soon as they came to the edge of the forest, they separated, each one going by himself in the old way, though now there was really no reason why they should have secrets from one another.

Ten minutes later, if you had been in the forest, you

might have seen the children standing in dismay with tears on their faces, and exclaiming that there had never been such a Christmas Eve before. For as they looked eagerly about them to the low-bending branches of the evergreen trees, they saw nothing hanging from them that could not be seen every day in the year. High and low they searched, wandering farther into the forest than ever before, lest Grandfather Christmas might have chosen a new place this year for hanging his presents; but still no presents appeared. The king called his counselors about him and asked them if they knew whether anything of this kind had happened before, but they could tell him nothing. So no one could guess whether Grandfather Christmas had forgotten them, or whether some dreadful accident had kept him away.

As the children were trooping out of the forest, after hours of weary searching, some of them came upon little Inge, who carried over his shoulder a bag that seemed to be full to overflowing. When he saw them looking at him, he cried:

"Are they not beautiful things? I think Grandfather Christmas was never so good to us before."

"Why, what do you mean?" cried the children. "There are no presents in the forest."

"No presents!" said Inge. "I have my bag full of them." But he did not offer to show them, because he did not want the children to see that they were all for his little sister instead of for himself.

Then the children begged him to tell them in what part of the forest he had found his presents, and he turned back and pointed them to the place where he had been. "I left many more behind than I brought away," he said.

"There they are! I can see some of the things shining on the trees even from here."

But when the children followed his footprints in the snow to the place where he had been, they still saw nothing on the trees, and thought that Inge must be walking in his sleep, and dreaming that he had found presents. Perhaps he had filled his bag with the cones from the evergreen trees.

On Christmas Day there was sadness all through The Great Walled Country. But those who came to the house of Inge and his sister saw plenty of books and dolls and beautiful toys piled up about the little cripple's chair; and when they asked where these things came from, they were told, "Why, from the Christmas-tree forest." And they shook their heads, not knowing what it could mean.

The king held a council in the palace and appointed a committee of his most faithful courtiers to visit Grandfather Christmas and see if they could find what was the matter. In a day or two more the committee set out on their journey. They had very hard work to climb the great wall of ice that lay between their country and the place where Grandfather Christmas lived, but at last they reached the top. And when they came to the other side of the wall, they were looking down into the top of his chimney. It was not hard to go down this chimney into the house, and when they reached the bottom of it they found themselves in the very room where Grandfather Christmas lay sound asleep.

It was hard enough to waken him, for he always slept one hundred days after his Christmas work was over, and it was only by turning the hands of the clock around two hundred times that the committee could do anything.

When the clock had struck twelve times two hundred hours, Grandfather Christmas thought it was time for his nap to be over, and he sat up in bed, rubbing his eyes.

"Oh, sir!" cried the prince who was in charge of the committee, "we have come from the king of The Great Walled Country, who has sent us to ask why you forgot us this Christmas, and left no presents in the forest."

"No presents!" said Grandfather Christmas. "I never forget anything. The presents were there. You did not see them, that's all."

But the children told him that they had searched long and carefully, and in the whole forest there had not been found a thing that could be called a Christmas gift.

"Indeed!" said Grandfather Christmas. "And did little Inge, the boy with the crippled sister, find none?"

Then the committee was silent, for they had heard of the gifts at Inge's house, and did not know what to say about them.

"You had better go home," said Grandfather Christmas, who now began to realize that he had been awakened too soon, "and let me finish my nap. The presents were there, but they were never intended for children who were looking only for themselves. I am not surprised that you could not see them. Remember that not everything that wise travelers tell you is wise." And he turned over and went to sleep again.

The committee returned silently to The Great Walled Country, and told the king what they had heard. The king did not tell all the children of the land what Grandfather Christmas had said, but, when the next December came, he made another proclamation, bidding everyone to seek gifts for others, in the old way, in the Christmas-tree forest. So that is what they have been doing ever since; and in order that they may not forget what happened, in case anyone should ever ask for another change, they have read to them every year from their Big Book the story of the time when they had no Christmas gifts.

——*Raymond Alden*

Kriss Kringle

Just as the moon was fading amid her misty rings,
And every stocking was stuffed with childhood's precious
    things,
Old Kriss Kringle looked round, and saw on an elm-tree
    bough,
High-hung, an oriole's nest, silent and empty now.
"Quite like a stocking," he laughed, "pinned up there on
    the tree!
Little I thought the birds expected a present from me!"
Then old Kriss Kringle who loves a joke as well as the
    best,
Dropped a handful of flakes in the oriole's empty nest.
                              ——*Thomas Bailey Aldrich*

The Tree that Trimmed Itself

"I WISH, OH, how I wish!" sighed the young Pine Tree, as Christmas wind blew through its branches, "that I might be a Christmas Tree with decorations like my brother who was cut down!"

The forest was very still and cold. It was Christmas Eve, the season of wonder, but very few trees had been cut for the children. So many tall, strong ones would be needed for building homes and for kindling fires and for making furniture. But, oh, the happiness of a Christmas Tree sparkling in the light of the home fire, with a circle of happy children dancing about it! No wonder that the young Pine Tree sighed again in the wind.

"The Tree that Trimmed Itself" by Carolyn Sherwin Bailey, is from *Merry Christmas Stories;* copyright, 1926, by Albert Whitman & Company; reprinted by permission.

"I wish that I might be trimmed for Christmas!" it whispered.

Suddenly something happened there in the woods. Floating down among the outspread branches of the Pine Tree came white stars, shaped like shining crystals.

More and then still more snow stars fell, until every twig of every branch of the tree held its white star.

They were more beautiful than any ornaments that the toyman had for trimming a Christmas Tree.

But still the young Pine Tree longed for all the honors his brother tree would have. "I wish that I might hear the Christmas Chimes!" it sighed in the wind.

Then the night grew colder and colder. The frost came through the forest and stopped beside the Pine Tree, hanging sharp, hard icicles to the tips of the twigs.

Whenever the wind touched the tree the icicles tinkled and rang like a chime of tiny Christmas bells. They made soft, beautiful Christmas music.

But still the young Pine Tree was not satisfied. "I wish," it sighed, "that I might hold lights as my brother will on this Christmas Eve."

Suddenly the stars shone out in the darkness and dropped their beams of light down as far as the branches of the young Pine Tree. One star seemed to leave the sky and rest on the topmost twig of the Pine Tree. There it flamed and flashed like a beacon to call everyone to see the wonders of Christmas Eve. The Pine Tree was lighted as brightly as if it carried a hundred candles, but still it had a wish.

"I am still not yet a Christmas Tree!" it sighed. "I wish that I might hold gifts among my branches." And it seemed as this wish could never come true, for where could Christmas gifts be found in the wintry forest?

Christmas Eve changed to the very early dawning of Christmas Day. Still the Pine Tree wore its snow stars. Its icicle chimes rang in the clear, cold air, and the light of the sky shone in its branches like a Christmas light. And out from the shelter of a nest among its roots crept a tiny mouse, cold and hungry.

How nice! Hanging to the Pine Tree, just above the nest of the mouse, was a bunch of berries and its trailing vine.

The vine had twisted itself around the trunk of the Tree in the summertime and now, in the deep winter, its bright berries hung there, a gift on Christmas morning for the hungry little mouse.

And out from the shelter of the trunk of the Pine Tree came a Squirrel. He, too, was hungry. But he scampered along the branch until he came to the part of the Tree where it had held tightly, in spite of the winter gales, a fat brown cone.

The squirrel held the cone daintily in his paws, cut out the seeds and munched them.

It was his holiday breakfast and how good it tasted! No better Christmas gift could have come to the squirrel than that fat pine cone so full of seeds.

"Merry Christmas!" called the children, running to the woods later on the morning of Christmas Day. "Merry Christmas, little Pine Tree. We have brought a gift for your snow bird. We heard him calling yesterday."

In their red caps and mittens, the happy children came dancing through the woods with a bundle of ripe grain.

They reached up as far as they could and hung it by a gay red ribbon to one of the green branches of the little

Pine Tree. Then they exclaimed, and they stood farther back in the path, for the snow bird came out from an empty nest among the branches which grew thickest to feast on the grain.

"The snow bird rested in a cradle on Christmas Eve!" the children said to each other. "The little Pine Tree must have held that empty nest very closely all winter to give the snow bird a Christmas cradle!"

And the little Pine Tree stood straight and happy there in the woods on Christmas morning, for all of its wishes had come true. It had trimmed itself with stars and heard the chimes and had offered its gifts to its little neighbors of the forest. And still it could grow for the building of homes when it was an older, larger pine!

——*Carolyn Sherwin Bailey*

Christmas in the Woods

Tonight when the hoar frost falls in the wood,
And the rabbit cowers, and the squirrel is cold,
And the horned owl huddles against a star,
And the drifts are deep, and the year is old,
All shy creatures will think of Him.
The shivering mouse, the hare, the wild young fox,
The doe with the startled faun,
Will dream of gentleness and a Child:

The buck with budding horns will turn
His starry eyes to a silver hill tonight,
The chipmunk will awake and stir
And leave his burrow for the chill dark midnight,
And all timid things will pause and sigh, and sighing, bless
That Child who loves the trembling hearts,
The shy hearts of the wilderness.

—————*Frances Frost*

Christmas in the Woods, by Frances Frost; copyright, 1942, by Frances Frost;
this selection reprinted by permission of Harper and Brothers.

The Mouse that Didn't Believe in Santa Claus

THE CLOCK STOOD, of course, in the corner, a moonbeam floated idly on the floor, and a little mauve mouse came from the hole in the chimney corner and frisked and scampered in the light of the moonbeam upon the floor. The little mauve mouse was particularly merry; sometimes she danced upon two legs and sometimes upon four legs, but always very daintily and always very merrily.

"Ah, me!" sighed the old clock, "how different mice are nowadays from the mice we used to have in the good old times! Now there was your grandma, Mistress Velvetpaw, and there was your grandpa, Master Sniffwhisker, —how grave and dignified they were! Many a night have I seen them dancing upon the carpet below me, but always the stately minuet and never that crazy frisking which you are executing now, to my surprise—yes, and to my horror, too."

"But why shouldn't I be merry?" asked the little mauve mouse. "To-morrow is Christmas, and this is Christmas Eve."

"So it is," said the old clock. "I had really forgotten all about it. But, tell me, what is Christmas to you, little Miss Mauve Mouse?"

"A great deal to me!" cried the little mauve mouse. "I have been very good a very long time: I have not used any bad words, nor have I gnawed any holes, nor have I stolen any canary seed, nor have I worried my mother by running behind the flour-barrel where that horrid trap is set. In fact, I have been so good that I'm very sure Santa Claus will bring me something very pretty."

This seemed to amuse the old clock mightily; in fact, the old clock fell to laughing so heartily that in an unguarded moment she struck twelve instead of ten, which was exceedingly careless and therefore to be reprehended.

"Why, you silly little mauve mouse," said the old clock, "you don't believe in Santa Claus, do you?"

"Of course I do," answered the little mauve mouse. "Believe in Santa Claus? Why shouldn't I? Didn't Santa Claus bring me a beautiful butter-cracker last Christmas, and a lovely gingersnap, and a delicious rind of cheese, and—and—lots of things? I should be very ungrateful if I did not believe in Santa Claus, and I certainly shall not disbelieve in him at the very moment when I am expecting him to arrive with a bundle of goodies for me."

"I once had a little sister," continued the little mauve mouse, "who did not believe in Santa Claus, and the very thought of the fate that befell her makes my blood run cold and my whiskers stand on end. She died before I was born, but my mother has told me all about her. Perhaps you never saw her; her name was Squeaknibble, and she was in stature one of those long, low, rangy mice that are seldom found in well-stocked pantries. Mother says that Squeaknibble took after our ancestors who came from New England, where the malignant ingenuity of the people and the ferocity of the cats rendered life precarious indeed. Squeaknibble seemed to inherit many ancestral traits, the most conspicuous of which was a disposition to sneer at some of the most respected dogmas in mousedom. From her very infancy she doubted, for example, the widely accepted theory that the moon was composed of green cheese; and this heresy was the first intimation her parents had of the sceptical turn of her mind. Of course, her parents were vastly annoyed, for their maturer natures saw that this youthful scepticism portended serious, if not fatal, consequences. Yet all in vain did the sagacious couple reason and plead with their headstrong and heretical child.

"For a long time Squeaknibble would not believe that there was any such archfiend as a cat; but she came to be convinced to the contrary one memorable night, on which occasion she lost two inches of her beautiful tail, and received so terrible a fright that for fully an hour afterward her little heart beat so violently as to lift her off her feet and bump her head against the top of our domestic hole. The cat that deprived my sister of so large a percentage of her vertebral colophon was the same brindled ogress that nowadays steals ever and anon into this room, crouches treacherously behind the sofa, and feigns to be asleep, hoping, forsooth, that some of us, heedless of her hated presence, will venture within reach of her diabolical claws. So enraged was this ferocious monster at the escape of my sister that she ground her fangs viciously together, and vowed to take no pleasure in life until she held in her devouring jaws the innocent little mouse which belonged to the mangled bit of tail she even then clutched in her remorseless claws."

"Yes," said the old clock, "now that you recall the incident, I recollect it well. I was here then, in this very corner, and I remember that I laughed at the cat and chided her for her awkwardness. My reproaches irritated her; she told me that a clock's duty was to run itself down not to be depreciating the merits of others! Yes, I recall the time; that cat's tongue is fully as sharp as her claws."

"Be that as it may," said the little mauve mouse, "it is a matter of history, and therefore beyond dispute, that from that very moment the cat pined for Squeaknibble's life; it seemed as if that one little two-inch taste of Squeaknibble's tail had filled the cat with a consuming passion, or appetite, for the rest of Squeaknibble. So the cat waited and watched and hunted and schemed and devised and did everything possible for a cat—a cruel cat—to do in order to gain her murderous ends. One night—one fatal Christmas eve—our mother had undressed the children for bed, and was urging upon them to go to sleep earlier than usual, since she fully expected that Santa Claus would bring each of them something very palatable and nice before morning. Thereupon the little dears whisked their cunning tails, pricked up their beautiful ears, and began telling one another what they hoped Santa Claus would bring. One asked for a slice of Roquefort, another for Neufchatel, another for Sap Sago, and a fourth Edam; one expressed a preference for de Brie, while another

hoped to get Parmesan; one clamored for imperial blue
Stilton, and another craved the fragrant boon of Caprera.
There were fourteen little ones then, and consequently
there were diverse opinions as to the kind of gift which
Santa Claus should best bring; still, there was, as you
can readily understand, an enthusiastic unanimity upon
this point, namely, that the gift should be cheese of some
brand or other.

" 'My dears,' said our mother, 'what matters it whether
the boon which Santa Claus brings be royal English
cheddar or fromage de Bricquebec, Vermont sage, or
Herkimer County skim-milk? We should be content with
whatsoever Santa Claus bestows, so long as it be cheese,
disjoined from all traps whatsoever, unmixed with Paris
green, and free from glass, strychnine, and other harmful
ingredients. As for myself, I shall be satisfied with a cut
of nice, fresh Western reserve; for truly I recognize in
no other viand or edible half the fragrance or half the
gustfulness to be met with in one of these pale but aromatic
domestic products. So run away to your dreams now, that
Santa Claus may find you sleeping.'

"The children obeyed,—all but Squeaknibble. 'Let the
others think what they please,' said she, 'but I don't believe in Santa Claus. I'm not going to bed, either. I'm
going to creep out of this dark hole and have a quiet romp,
all by myself, in the moonlight.' Oh, what a vain, foolish,
wicked little mouse was Squeaknibble! But I will not
reproach the dead; her punishment came all too swiftly.
Now listen: who do you suppose overheard her talking
so disrespectfully of Santa Claus?"

"Why, Santa Claus himself," said the old clock.

"Oh, no," answered the little mauve mouse. "It was

that wicked, murderous cat! Just as Satan lurks and lies in wait for bad children, so does the cruel cat lurk and lie in wait for naughty little mice. And you can depend upon it that, when that awful cat heard Squeaknibble speak so disrespectfully of Santa Claus, her wicked eyes glowed with joy, her sharp teeth watered, and her bristling fur emitted electric sparks as big as marrowfat peas. Then what did that blood-thirsty monster do but scuttle as fast as she could into Dear-my-Soul's room, leap up into Dear-my-Soul's crib, and walk off with the pretty little white muff which Dear-my-Soul used to wear when she went for a visit to the little girl in the next block! What upon earth did the horrid old cat want with Dear-my-Soul's pretty little white muff? Ah, the duplicity, the diabolical ingenuity of that! Listen.

"In the first place," resumed the little mauve mouse, after a pause that testified eloquently to the depth of her emotion,—"in the first place, that wretched cat dressed herself up in that pretty little white muff, by which you are to understand that she crawled through the muff just so far as to leave her four cruel legs at liberty."

"Yes, I understand," said the old clock.

"Then she put on the boy doll's fur cap," said the little mauve mouse, "and when she was arrayed in the boy doll's fur cap and Dear-my-Soul's pretty little white muff, of course she didn't look like a cruel cat at all. But whom did she look like?"

"Like the boy doll," suggested the old clock.

"No, no!" cried the little mauve mouse.

"Like Dear-my-Soul?" asked the old clock.

"How stupid you are!" exclaimed the little mauve mouse. "Why, she looked like Santa Claus, of course!"

"Oh, yes; I see," said the old clock. "Now I begin to be interested; go on."

"Alas!" sighed the little mauve mouse, "not much remains to be told; but there is more of my story left than there was of Squeaknibble when that horrid cat crawled out of that miserable disguise. You are to understand that, contrary to her sagacious mother's injunction, and in notorious derision of the mooted coming of Santa Claus, Squeaknibble issued from the friendly hole in the chimney corner, and gamboled about over this very carpet, and, I dare say, in this very moonlight.

"Right merrily was Squeaknibble gamboling," continued the little mauve mouse, "and she had just turned a double back somersault without the use of what remained of her tail, when, all of a sudden, she beheld, looming up like a monster ghost, a figure all in white fur! Oh, how frightened she was, and how her little heart did beat! 'Purr, purr-r-r,' said the ghost in white fur. 'Oh, please don't hurt me!' pleaded Squeaknibble. 'No; I'll not hurt you,' said the ghost in white fur; 'I'm Santa Claus, and I've brought you a beautiful piece of savory old cheese, you dear little mousie, you.' Poor Squeaknibble was deceived; a sceptic all her life, she was at last befooled by the most palpable and most fatal of frauds. 'How good of you!' said Squeaknibble. 'I didn't believe there was a Santa Claus, and—' but before she could say more she was seized by two sharp, cruel claws that conveyed her crushed body to the murderous mouth of mousedom's most malignant foe. I can dwell no longer upon this harrowing scene. Suffice it to say that ere the morrow's sun rose like a big yellow Herkimer County cheese upon the spot where that tragedy had been enacted, poor

Squeaknibble passed to that bourn whence two inches of her beautiful tail had preceded her by the space of three weeks to a day. As for Santa Claus, when he came that Christmas eve, bringing morceaux de Brie and of Stilton for the other little mice, he heard with sorrow of Squeaknibble's fate; and ere he departed he said that in all his experience he had never known of a mouse or of a child that had prospered after once saying that he didn't believe in Santa Claus."

——*Eugene Field*

The Gift of St. Nicholas

THREE HUNDRED YEARS AGO in the little city of
New Amsterdam lived a young cobbler named Claas. A
fortunate fellow indeed was Claas. He had a lovely brick
house with a garden, a big pond full of fat white geese, a
thriving trade, and a pretty wife whose name was Anitje.
He had worked hard for these blessings from the first bleak
day when he landed on the shores of the New World, an
orphan boy from Holland. He was now a rich man, rich
enough to wear eight pairs of breeches at once.

The only dark cloud in his sky was Roeloffsen, the
burgomaster, an old miser who had long been in love with
Anitje. As the richest old bachelor in the town, he had

expected her to marry him without question. When she married the poor cobbler boy, the burgomaster's pride was hurt. He swore that he should have his revenge. When ever Claas and Anitje walked out in their Sunday clothes, their family of fat Dutch children toddling behind them, he hid behind the heavy curtains of his house and said terrible things.

At last his ugly thoughts were put into deeds. He taught the village blacksmith to make hobnails for the towns-people's boots. These nails made a dreadful racket as they clattered over the brick streets. But they kept the boots from wearing out. The boots wore so long that poor Claas had very little business as a cobbler. He had a very hard time to make ends meet.

This was not enough for the black-hearted burgomaster, however. Claas and his Anitje still lived in their fine brick house and walked out Sundays in their handsome clothes. Roeloffsen had to think of something else.

Soon he knew what to do. As an officer of the city he ordered a new street to be built. This street ran right through the middle of Claas's pond. The city builders came and drained the pond. Poor Claas had to sell his beloved geese. This was a great blow to him, because the eggs he sold at the market place helped make up for the boots he was unable to sell.

But this was not the worst of it. As Claas sat by his fire sorrowing for the loss of his geese, he had visitors. These were men from the city council. Since the road ran through his land, they said, he should pay for its building. They demanded fifty pieces of gold for this purpose. Fifty pieces of gold! That was all Claas had tucked away in his teapot.

Claas and Anitje had to work harder than ever to keep their family fed and clothed. They sold vegetables from their garden and managed to make themselves a fair living. Then came the jealous burgomaster. He built another road, through the middle of Claas's garden patch this time. Once again the poor cobbler had to rob his teapot in order to pay for this road.

And so it went. Every time Claas made a little money, the burgomaster built a new road and made him pay for it. Before long he had to sell his fine house. No longer could he afford to wear eight pair of breeches, nor Anitje her twelve petticoats. The little family was poor. They had sold all their belongings except a bare few. They lived in a miserable little cottage with only a dirt floor.

The wicked old burgomaster at last was satisfied. He danced with joy when he saw how low the cobbler had fallen. This would show the people of New Amsterdam that no orphan boy could outdo the wealthy Heer Roeloffsen!

On Christmas Eve, as the burgomaster was enjoying his fine dinner, Claas and Anitje and their children sat huddled before the fireplace in their little cottage. The very last log burned on the hearth and gave out little heat at best. Their cupboard, like old Mother Hubbard's, was bare. After their supper of bread and cheese, not a crumb remained. A poor Christmas this would be. No presents, no blazing fire, not even a dinner.

Of all their possessions, only two treasures remained. One was the Bible which Claas's mother had given him long ago. It was bound in a beautiful leather and held shut with silver clasps. Claas was tempted to take off these clasps and sell them. They might bring him enough money to provide a Christmas for his children.

No! said Anitje. To sell the clasps from a Bible would be wicked. He should never think of doing such a thing. Better it would be to starve than to feast on the sale of holy things.

The other treasure which remained was a pipe. This was a special, lovely pure meerschaum pipe which to Claas had a magic meaning. As a little boy, leaving his home for the New World, he had found the pipe in his stocking. Where it had come from he could not tell. He was sure it was a present from the good Saint Nicholas himself.

As he rubbed it the cottage door swung open and a blast of cold air filled the room. There before the fire stood a fat little stranger, about three feet tall. He was dripping with snow, and icicles hung from his shaggy eyebrows and long white beard.

"Br-r-r!" muttered the stranger crossly. "It's a wonder you wouldn't answer the door when a traveler knocks. Fine manners, I must say, on a night like this!"

All thoughts of the pipe were forgotten as Claas and Anitje stared at their visitor. The children scrambled to hide under the bed. Only their blue eyes shone out from behind the curtains.

"Well, come along! Come along!" went on the visitor, growing more angry every minute. "Don't stand there! The least you can do is to put another log on the fire so that I can warm myself. Can't you see I'm half frozen?"

"I-I-I-I'm very sorry, sir," admitted Claas, finding his tongue at last, "but there is not another log to put on the fire. You're very welcome to warm yourself at our poor hearth."

"Well, then," snapped the stranger, "send one of those ragamuffins out to the woodshed. I'm freezing, I tell you!" He glared at the children, who pushed themselves farther back under the bed hangings.

"Oh sir!" cried Anitje, "if only we had more wood in the shed we would gladly fetch it for you. But alas, this is our last stick. We have no more to keep ourselves warm."

"Humph!" snorted the little fellow. "That's very careless of you. But what must be, must be!" With that he cracked the fine cane he carried over his knee. It broke into several pieces. These he tossed onto the coals. As they struck the fire, something wonderful happened. Each of the pieces of cane changed into a big birch log. The dark coals blazed up and soon the room was dancing with the light of a huge fire.

"That's better," muttered the stranger. "Upon my life, I thought I should turn into an icicle for all you cared."

The children crept out of their hiding place to gape at the magic blaze. Claas and Anitje rubbed their eyes.

"And now, I suppose, you're going to let me starve to death, too!" sneered the visitor, looking in the direction of the cupboard. "It's a wonder you wouldn't invite me to have some supper. I haven't eaten since this morning."

Tears came to Anitje's eyes. "Oh sir, whoever you may be, we would indeed be happy to give you our last crumb. But," she sobbed, "we have nothing to eat in the house. We ate our last scrap of cheese for our evening meal."

"That was certainly rude of you," barked the funny little man. "Here I come, after a hard day's tramp over the mountains, through wind and rain and snow! You say you have no bread to feed me! My dear lady, I know better.

Your shelves are heaped with cakes and apples. And if that's not roast goose I smell cooking, I'll eat my beard!"

Without thinking, the whole family stopped to sniff. Why, they did smell roast goose! And cabbage and onion and mince pie and pumpkin! These delicious smells were fairly bursting from the oven door. They looked quickly at the cupboard. Its shelves were groaning under bowls of apples and pears and platters of cakes and cookies. The water jug was filled to the brim with sweet cider.

"Don't stand there, don't stand there like a forest of trees!" shouted the stranger. "Can't you see I'm dying of hunger? Get me something to eat and be quick about it. No food indeed! Why, there's a whole feast in that oven. Put it on the table."

Not knowing whether to be overjoyed or frightened, Claas and Anitje set the table and drew it before the fire. They opened the wide door of the oven. There indeed were the goose and the vegetables and the pies they smelled.

At the sight of the richly spread table, the children forgot their shyness. Hungrily they feasted. But none of them ate so much as did their visitor. Time and again he passed back his plate for another drumstick. An ordinary goose has only two legs, but this one sprouted a new one whenever the little man passed his plate.

When at last the fat little stranger had had enough and the buttons began to burst from Claas's coat, the table was cleared away. No longer did the visitor snap angrily at his hosts. He leaned back in his chair and lit his pipe. A twinkle appeared in his eye and he patted the children's blond heads. For an hour he sat talking pleasantly with the happy family, telling them strange and marvelous tales of distant lands. But not once did he tell them who he was.

At the stroke of midnight he got up from his chair. "I must be off!" he exclaimed. "Thank you indeed for a pleasant evening and a delicious dinner." He turned to Claas. "Don't ever sell that pipe," he shouted.

In the morning Claas was awakened by a great hammering at his door. There was Burgomaster Roeloffsen and a party of soldiers. "We have come to arrest you!" they screamed. "You are a wizard, a witch, a magician. You are a disgrace to the city of New Amsterdam."

Poor Claas didn't know what to make of it. Why should anyone call him a wizard. He was nothing but a poor cobbler who had had a lovely dream.

"Come!" roared the burgomaster. "Open the door and let us in. We shall have no wizards in our city!"

As he slowly wakened, Claas looked about him. The wretched little cottage had disappeared. He was standing in the door of a great house. The walls were hung with silk, and from the cupboards shone silver platters and copper bowls. He looked timidly out of the window. Around him spread wide lawns and gardens and in the distance glimmered the ice of a huge pond.

"Open up, I say," bellowed the burgomaster. "Open up in the name of the law. We have come to take you to jail as you deserve." Claas opened the door. In poured the soldiers.

"Aha!" screamed Heer Roeloffsen, his face red with anger. "Seize him! Seize the witch! He has not only changed his cottage to a fine estate. He has filled his chests with gold."

Before the astonished Claas the burgomaster lifted the

lid of a chest. The great box was full to the top with pieces of money.

"You thief! You robber! I'll . . ." But before he could finish his sentence, a pair of invisible hands clapped themselves over his mouth. More hands which could not be seen grabbed the soldiers. Then came an awful whacking and thrashing as the unseen arms paddled the burgomaster and his party with unseen switches.

"Ouch! Help! Stop it!" yelled Roeloffsen. But the paddling went on. The soldiers ran down the path to the main road and headed away from town, crying and yelling and trying to defend themselves from the blows of the unseen paddlers.

That was the last ever seen of the jealous burgomaster. Claas and his family lived on in their fine new home, never wanting for food or warmth. How their good fortune had come they did not know. The only clue they had was a piece of paper slipped under the door. It said simply, "Don't ever sell that pipe."

——*Anne Malcolmson*

Dulce Domum

THE SHEEP RAN huddling together against the hurdles, blowing out thin nostrils and stamping with delicate fore-feet, their heads thrown back and a light steam rising from the crowded sheep-pen into the frosty air, as the two animals hastened by in high spirits, with much chatter and laughter. They were returning across country after a long day's outing with Otter, hunting and exploring on the wide uplands where certain streams tributary to their own river had their first small beginnings; and the shades of the short winter day were closing in on them, and they had still some distance to go. Plodding at random across the plough, they had heard the sheep and had made for them; and now, leading from the sheep-pen, they found a beaten track that made walking a lighter business, and responded, moreover, to that small inquiring something which all animals carry inside them, saying unmistakably, "Yes, quite right; this leads home!"

"It looks as if we were coming to a village," said the Mole somewhat dubiously, slackening his pace, as the track, that had in time become a path and then had developed into a lane, now handed them over to the charge of a well-metalled road. The animals did not hold with villages, and their own highways, thickly frequented as they were, took an independent course, regardless of church, post office, or public-house.

"Oh, never mind!" said the Rat. "At this season of the year they're all safe indoors by this time, sitting round the fire; men, women, and children, dogs and cats and all. We shall slip through all right, without any bother or unpleasantness, and we can have a look at them through their windows if you like, and see what they're doing."

The rapid nightfall of mid-December had quite beset the little village as they approached it on soft feet over a first thin fall of powdery snow. Little was visible but squares of a dusky orange-red on either side of the street, where the firelight or lamplight of each cottage overflowed through the casements into the dark world without. Most of the low latticed windows were innocent of blinds, and to the lookers-in from outside, the inmates, gathered round the tea-table, absorbed in handiwork, or talking with laughter and gesture, had each that happy grace which is the last thing the skilled actor shall capture— the natural grace which goes with perfect unconsciousness of observation. Moving at will from one theatre to another, the two spectators, so far from home themselves, had something of wistfulness in their eyes as they watched a cat being stroked, a sleepy child picked up and huddled off to bed, or a tired man stretch and knock out his pipe on the end of a smouldering log.

But it was from one little window, with its blind drawn down, a mere blank transparency on the night, that the sense of home and the little curtained world within walls —the larger stressful world of outside Nature shut out and forgotten—most pulsated. Close against the white blind hung a bird-cage, clearly silhouetted, every wire, perch, and appurtenance distinct and recognizable, even to yesterday's dull-edged lump of sugar. On the middle perch the fluffy occupant, head tucked well into feathers, seemed so near to them as to be easily stroked, had they tried; even the delicate tips of his plumped-out plumage pencilled plainly on the illuminated screen. As they looked, the sleepy little fellow stirred uneasily, woke, shook himself, and raised his head. They could see the gape of his tiny beak as he yawned in a bored sort of way, looked round, and then settled his head into his back again, while the ruffled feathers gradually subsided into perfect stillness. Then a gust of bitter wind took them in the back of the neck, a small sting of frozen sleet on the skin woke them as from a dream, and they knew their toes to be cold and their legs tired, and their own home distant a weary way.

Once beyond the village, where the cottages ceased abruptly, on either side of the road they could smell through the darkness the friendly fields again; and they braced themselves for the last long stretch, the home stretch, the stretch that we know is bound to end, some time, in the rattle of the door-latch, the sudden firelight, and the sight of familiar things greeting us as long-absent travellers from far oversea. They plodded along steadily and silently, each of them thinking his own thoughts. The Mole's ran a good deal on supper, as it was pitch-dark, and it was all a strange country to him as far as he knew, and he was following obediently in the wake of the Rat, leaving the guidance entirely to him. As for the Rat, he was walking a little way ahead, as his habit was, his shoulders humped, his eyes fixed on the straight grey road in front of him; so he did not notice poor Mole when suddenly the summons reached him, and took him like an electric shock.

We others, who have long lost the more subtle of the physical senses, have not even proper terms to express an animal's intercommunications with his surroundings, living or otherwise, and have only the word "smell," for instance, to include the whole range of delicate thrills which murmur in the nose of the animal night and day, summoning, warning, inciting, repelling. It was one of these mysterious fairy calls from out the void that suddenly reached Mole in the darkness, making him tingle through and through with its very familiar appeal, even while as yet he could not clearly remember what it was. He stopped dead in his tracks, his nose searching hither and thither in its efforts to recapture the fine filament, the telegraphic current, that had so strongly moved him. A moment, and he had caught it again; and with it this time came recollection in fullest flood.

Home! That was what they meant, those caressing appeals, those soft touches wafted through the air, those invisible little hands pulling and tugging, all one way! Why, it must be quite close by him at that moment, his old home that he had hurriedly forsaken and never sought again, that day when he first found the river! And now it was sending out its scouts and its messengers to capture him and bring him in. Since his escape on that bright morning he had hardly given it a thought, so absorbed had he been in his new life, in all its pleasures, it surprises, its fresh and captivating experiences. Now, with a rush of old memories, how clearly it stood up before him, in the darkness! Shabby indeed, and small and poorly furnished, and yet his, the home he had made for himself, the home he had been so happy to get back to after his day's work. And the home had been happy with him, too, evidently, and was missing him, and wanted him back, and was telling him so, through his nose, sorrowfully, reproachfully, but with no bitterness or anger; only with plaintive reminder that it was there, and wanted him.

The call was clear, the summons was plain. He must obey it instantly, and go. "Ratty!" he called, full of joyful excitement, "hold on! Come back! I want you quick!"

"O, come along, Mole, do!" replied the Rat cheerfully, still plodding along.

"Please stop, Ratty!" pleaded the poor Mole, in anguish of heart. "You don't understand! It's my home, my old home! I've just come across the smell of it, and it's close by here, really quite close. And I must go to it, I must, I must! O, come back, Ratty! Please, please come back!"

The Rat was by this time very far ahead, too far to hear clearly what the Mole was calling, too far to catch the sharp note of painful appeal in his voice. And he was much taken up with the weather, for he too could smell something—something suspiciously like approaching snow.

"Mole, we mustn't stop now, really!" he called back. "We'll come for it tomorrow, whatever it is you've found.

But I daren't stop now—it's late, and the snow's coming on again, and I'm not sure of the way! And I want your nose, Mole, so come on quick, there's a good fellow!" And the Rat pressed forward on his way without waiting for an answer.

Poor Mole stood alone in the road, his heart torn asunder, and a big sob gathering, gathering, somewhere low down inside him, to leap up to the surface presently, he knew, in passionate escape. But even under such a test as this his loyalty to his friend stood firm. Never for a moment did he dream of abandoning him. Meanwhile, the wafts from his old home pleaded, whispered, conjured, and finally claimed him imperiously. He dared not tarry longer within their magic circle. With a wrench that tore his very heartstrings he set his face down the road and followed submissively in the track of the Rat, while faint, thin little smells, still dogging his retreating nose, reproached him for his new friendship and his callous forgetfulness.

With an effort he caught up the unsuspecting Rat, who began chattering cheerfully about what they would do when they got back, and how jolly a fire of logs in the parlour would be, and what a supper he meant to eat; never noticing his companion's silence and distressful state of mind. At last, however, when they had gone some considerable way further, and were passing some tree-stumps at the edge of a copse that bordered the road, he stopped and said kindly, "Look here, Mole, old chap, you seem dead tired. No talk left in you, and your feet dragging like lead. We'll sit down here for a minute and rest. The snow has held off so far, and the best part of our journey is over."

The Mole subsided forlornly on a tree-stump and tried to control himself, for he felt it surely coming. The sob he had fought with so long refused to be beaten. Up and up, it forced its way to the air, and then another, and another, and others thick and fast; till poor Mole at last gave up the struggle, and cried freely and helplessly and openly, now that he knew it was all over and he had lost what he could hardly be said to have found.

The Rat, astonished and dismayed at the violence of Mole's paroxysm of grief, did not dare to speak for a while. At last he said, very quietly and sympathetically, "What is it, old fellow? Whatever can be the matter? Tell us your trouble, and let me see what I can do."

Poor Mole found it difficult to get any words out between the upheavals of his chest that followed one upon another so quickly and held back speech and choked it as it came. "I know it's a—shabby, dingy little place," he sobbed forth at last, brokenly: "not like—your cosy quarters—or Toad's beautiful hall—or Badger's great house—but it was my own little home—and I was fond of it—and I went away and forgot all about it—and then I smelt it suddenly—on the road, when I called and you wouldn't listen, Rat—and everything came back to me with a rush—and I wanted it!—O dear, O dear!—and when you wouldn't turn back, Ratty—and I had to leave it, though I was smelling it all the time—I thought my heart would break.—We might have just gone and had one look at it, Ratty—only one look—it was close by— but you wouldn't turn back, Ratty, you wouldn't turn back! O dear, O dear!"

Recollection brought fresh waves of sorrow, and sobs again took full charge of him, preventing further speech.

The Rat stared straight in front of him, saying nothing, only patting Mole gently on the shoulder. After a time he muttered gloomily, "I see it all now! What a pig I have been! A pig—that's me! Just a pig—a plain pig!"

He waited till Mole's sobs became gradually less stormy and more rhythmical; he waited till at last sniffs were frequent and sobs only intermittent. Then he rose from his seat, and, remarking carelessly, "Well, now we'd really better be getting on, old chap!" set off up the road again, over the toilsome way they had come.

"Wherever are you (hic) going to (hic), Ratty?" cried the tearful Mole, looking up in alarm.

"We're going to find that home of yours, old fellow," replied the Rat pleasantly; "so you had better come along, for it will take some finding, and we shall want your nose."

"O, come back, Ratty, do!" cried the Mole, getting up and hurrying after him. "It's no good, I tell you! It's too late, and too dark, and the place is too far off, and the snow's coming! And—and I never meant to let you know I was feeling that way about it—it was all an accident and a mistake! And think of River Bank, and your supper!"

"Hang River Bank, and supper too!" said the Rat heartily. "I tell you, I'm going to find this place now, if I stay out all night. So cheer up, old chap, and take my arm, and we'll very soon be back there again."

Still snuffling, pleading, and reluctant, Mole suffered himself to be dragged back along the road by his imperious companion, who by a flow of cheerful talk and anecdote endeavoured to beguile his spirits back and make the weary way seem shorter. When at last it seemed to

the Rat that they must be nearing that part of the road
where the Mole had been "held up," he said, "Now, no
more talking. Business! Use your nose, and give your
mind to it."

They moved on in silence for some little way, when
suddenly the Rat was conscious, through his arm that was
linked in Mole's, of a faint sort of electric thrill that
was passing down that animal's body. Instantly he dis-
engaged himself, fell back a pace, and waited, all attention.

The signals were coming through!

Mole stood a moment rigid, while his uplifted nose,
quivering slightly, felt the air.

Then a short, quick run forward—a fault—a check—a
try back; and then a slow, steady, confident advance.

The Rat, much excited, kept close to his heels as the
Mole, with something of the air of a sleepwalker, crossed
a dry ditch, scrambled through a hedge, and nosed his
way over a field open and trackless and bare in the faint
starlight.

Suddenly, without giving warning, he dived; but the
Rat was on the alert, and promptly followed him down
the tunnel to which his unerring nose had faithfully
led him.

It was close and airless, and the earthy smell was strong,
and it seemed a long time to Rat ere the passage ended
and he could stand erect and stretch and shake himself.
The Mole struck a match, and by its light the Rat saw
that they were standing in an open space, neatly swept
and sanded underfoot, and directly facing them was
Mole's little front door, with "Mole End" painted, in
Gothic lettering, over the bell-pull at the side.

Mole reached down a lantern from a nail on the wall

and lit it, and the Rat, looking round him, saw that they were in a sort of fore-court. A garden-seat stood on one side of the door, and on the other, a roller; for the Mole, who was a tidy animal when at home, could not stand having his ground kicked up by other animals into little runs that ended in earth-heaps. On the walls hung wire baskets with ferns in them, alternating with brackets carrying plaster statuary—Garibaldi, and the infant Samuel, and Queen Victoria, and other heroes of modern Italy. Down one side of the fore-court ran a skittle-alley, with benches along it and little wooden tables marked with rings that hinted at beer-mugs. In the middle was a small round pond containing goldfish and surrounded by a cockle-shell border. Out of the centre of the pond rose a fanciful erection clothed in more cockle-shells and topped by a large silvered glass ball that reflected everything all wrong and had a very pleasing effect.

Mole's face beamed at the sight of all these objects so dear to him, and he hurried Rat through the door, lit a lamp in the hall, and took one glance round his old home. He saw the dust lying thick on everything, saw the cheerless, deserted look of the long-neglected house, and its narrow, meagre dimensions, its worn and shabby contents—and collapsed again on a hall-chair, his nose in his paws. "O, Ratty!" he cried dismally, "why ever did I do it? Why did I bring you to this poor, cold little place, on a night like this, when you might have been at River Bank by this time, toasting your toes before a blazing fire, with all your nice things about you!"

The Rat paid no heed to his doleful self-reproaches. He was running here and there, opening doors, inspecting rooms and cupboards, and lighting lamps and candles and sticking them up everywhere. "What a capital little house this is!" he called out cheerily. "So compact! So well planned! Everything here and everything in its place! We'll make a jolly night of it. The first thing we want is a good fire; I'll see to that—I always know where to find things. So this is the parlour? Splendid! Your own idea, those little sleeping-bunks in the wall? Capital! Now, I'll fetch the wood and the coals, and you get a duster, Mole—you'll find one in the drawer of the kitchen table—and try and smarten things up a bit. Bustle about, old chap!"

Encouraged by his inspiriting companion, the Mole roused himself and dusted and polished with energy and heartiness, while the Rat, running to and fro with armfuls of fuel, soon had a cheerful blaze roaring up the chimney. He hailed the Mole to come and warm himself; but Mole promptly had another fit of the blues, dropping down on a couch in dark despair and burying his face in his duster.

"Rat," he moaned, "how about your supper, you poor, cold, hungry, weary animal? I've nothing to give you—nothing—not a crumb!"

"What a fellow you are for giving in!" said the Rat reproachfully. "Why, only just now I saw a sardine-opener on the kitchen dresser, quite distinctly; and everybody knows that means there are sardines about somewhere in the neighbourhood. Rouse yourself! pull yourself together, and come with me and forage."

They went and foraged accordingly, hunting through every cupboard and turning out every drawer. The result was not so very depressing after all, though of course it might have been better; a tin of sardines—a box of captain's biscuits, nearly full—and a German sausage encased in silver paper.

"There's a banquet for you!" observed the Rat, as he arranged the table. "I know some animals who would give their ears to be sitting down to supper with us tonight!"

"No bread!" groaned the Mole dolorously; "no butter, no—"

"No pate de foie gras, no champagne!" continued the Rat, grinning. "And that reminds me—what's that little door at the end of the passage? Your cellar, of course! Every luxury in this house! Just you wait a minute."

He made for the cellar door, and presently reappeared, somewhat dusty, with a bottle of beer in each paw and another under each arm. "Self-indulgent beggar you seem to be, Mole," he observed. "Deny yourself nothing. This is really the jolliest little place I ever was in. Now, wherever did you pick up those prints? Make the place look so home-like, they do. No wonder you're so fond of it, Mole. Tell us all about it, and how you came to make it what it is."

Then, while the Rat busied himself fetching plates, and knives and forks, and mustard which he mixed in an egg-cup, the Mole, his bosom still heaving with the stress of his recent emotion, related—somewhat shyly at first, but with more freedom as he warmed to his subject—how this was planned, and how that was thought out, and how this was got through a windfall from an aunt, and that was a wonderful find and a bargain, and this other thing was bought out of laborious savings and a certain amount of "going without." His spirits finally quite restored, he must needs go and caress his possessions, and take a lamp and show off their points to his visitor and expatiate on them, quite forgetful of the supper they both so much needed; Rat, who was desperately hungry but strove to conceal it, nodding seriously, examining with a puckered brow, and saying, "Wonderful," and "Most remarkable," at intervals, when the chance for an observation was given him.

At last the Rat succeeded in decoying him to the table, and had just got seriously to work with the sardine-opener when sounds were heard from the fore-court with-out—sounds like the scuffling of small feet in the gravel and a confused murmur of tiny voices, while broken sentences reached them—"Now, all in a line—hold the lantern up a bit, Tommy—clear your throats first—no coughing after I say one, two, three.—Where's young Bill?—Here, come on, do, we're all a-waiting——"

"What's up?" inquired the Rat, pausing in his labours.

"I think it must be the field-mice," replied the Mole, with a touch of pride in his manner. "They go round carol-singing regularly at this time of the year. They're quite an institution in these parts. And they never pass me over—they come to Mole End last of all; and I used to give them hot drinks, and supper too sometimes, when I could afford it. It will be like old times to hear them again."

"Let's have a look at them!" cried the Rat, jumping up and running to the door.

It was a pretty sight, and a seasonable one, that met their eyes when they flung the door open. In the fore-court, lit by the dim rays of a horn lantern, some eight or ten little field-mice stood in a semi-circle, red worsted comforters round their throats, their fore-paws thrust deep into their pockets, their feet jigging for warmth. With bright beady eyes they glanced shyly at each other, sniggering a little, sniffing and applying coat-sleeves a good deal. As the door opened, one of the elder ones that carried the lantern was just saying, "Now then, one, two, three!" and forthwith their shrill little voices uprose on the air, singing one of the old-time carols that their forefathers composed in fields that were fallow and held by frost, or when snow-bound in chimney corners, and handed down to be sung in the miry street to lamp-lit windows at Yule-time.

CAROL

Villagers all, this frosty tide,
Let your doors swing open wide,
Though wind may follow, and snow beside,
Yet draw us in by your fire to bide;
    Joy shall be yours in the morning!

Here we stand in the cold and the sleet,
Blowing fingers and stamping feet,
Come from far away you to greet—
You by the fire and we in the street—
    Bidding you joy in the morning!

For ere one half of the night was gone,
Sudden a star has led us on,
Raining bliss and benison—
Bliss to-morrow and more anon,
    Joy for every morning!

Goodman Joseph toiled through the snow—
Saw the star o'er a stable low;
Mary she might not further go—
Welcome thatch, and litter below!
Joy was hers in the morning!

And then they heard the angels tell
"Who were the first to cry Nowell?
Animals all, as it befell,
In the stable where they did dwell!
Joy shall be theirs in the morning!"

The voices ceased, the singers, bashful but smiling, exchanged sidelong glances, and silence succeeded—but for a moment only. Then, from up above and far away, down the tunnel they had so lately travelled was borne to their ears in a faint musical hum the sound of distant bells ringing a joyful and clangorous peal.

"Very well sung, boys!" cried the Rat heartily. "And now come along in, all of you, and warm yourselves by the fire, and have something hot!"

"Yes, come along, field-mice," cried the Mole eagerly. "This is quite like old times! Shut the door after you. Pull up that settle to the fire. Now, you just wait a minute, while we—O, Ratty!" he cried in despair, plumping down on a seat, with tears impending. "Whatever are we doing? We've nothing to give them!"

"You leave all that to me," said the masterful Rat. "Here, you with the lantern! Come over this way. I want to talk to you. Now, tell me, are there any shops open at this hour of the night?"

"Why, certainly, sir," replied the field-mouse respect-
fully. "At this time of the year our shops keep open to
all sorts of hours."

"Then look here!" said the Rat. "You go off at once,
you and your lantern, and you get me—"

Here much muttered conversation ensued, and the
Mole only heard bits of it, such as—"Fresh, mind!—no,
a pound of that will do—see you get Buggins's, for I
won't have any other—no, only the best—if you can't get
it there, try somewhere else—yes, of course, home-made,
no tinned stuff—well then, do the best you can!" Finally,
there was a chink of coin passing from paw to paw, the
field-mouse was provided with an ample basket for his
purchases, and off he hurried, he and his lantern.

The rest of the field-mice, perched in a row on the settle,
their small legs swinging, gave themselves up to enjoy-
ment of the fire, and toasted their chilblains till they
tingled; while the Mole, failing to draw them into easy
conversation, plunged into family history and made each
of them recite the names of his numerous brothers, who
were too young, it appeared, to be allowed to go out
a-carolling this year, but looked forward very shortly to
winning the parental consent.

The Rat, meanwhile, was busy examining the label on
one of the beer-bottles. "I perceive this to be Old Burton,"
he remarked approvingly. "Sensible Mole! The very
thing! Now we shall be able to mull some ale! Get the
things ready, Mole, while I draw the corks."

It did not take long to prepare the brew and thrust the
tin heater well into the red heart of the fire; and soon
every field-mouse was sipping and coughing and choking

(for a little mulled ale goes a long way) and wiping his eyes and laughing and forgetting he had ever been cold in all his life.

"They act plays too, these fellows," the Mole explained to the Rat. "Make them up all by themselves, and act them afterwards. And very well they do it, too! They gave us a capital one last year, about a field-mouse who was captured at sea by a Barbary corsair, and made to row in a galley; and when he escaped and got home again, his lady-love had gone into a convent. Here, you! You were in it, I remember. Get up and recite a bit."

The field-mouse addressed got up on his legs, giggled shyly, looked round the room, and remained absolutely tongue-tied. His comrades cheered him on, Mole coaxed and encouraged him, and the Rat went so far as to take him by the shoulders and shake him; but nothing could overcome his stage-fright. They were all busily engaged on him like water men applying the Royal Humane Society's regulations to a case of long submersion, when the latch clicked, the door opened, and the field-mouse with the lantern reappeared, staggering under the weight of his basket.

There was no more talk of play-acting once the real and solid contents of the basket had been tumbled out on the table. Under the generalship of Rat, everybody was set to do something or to fetch something. In a very few minutes supper was ready, and Mole, as he took the head of the table in a sort of dream, saw a lately barren board set thick with savoury comforts; saw his little friends' faces brighten and beam as they fell to without delay; and then let himself loose—for he was famished indeed—on the provender so magically provided, thinking what a happy homecoming this had turned out, after all. As they ate, they talked of old times, and the field-mice gave him the local gossip up to date, and answered as well as they could the hundred questions he had to ask them. The Rat said little or nothing, only taking care that each guest had what he wanted, and plenty of it, and that Mole had no trouble or anxiety about anything.

They clattered off at last, very grateful and showering wishes of the season, with their jacket pockets stuffed with remembrances for the small brothers and sisters at home. When the door had closed on the last of them and the chink of the lanterns had died away, Mole and Rat kicked the fire up, drew their chairs in, brewed themselves a last nightcap of mulled ale, and discussed the events of the long day. At last the Rat, with a tremendous yawn, said, "Mole, old chap, I'm ready to drop. Sleepy is simply not the word. That your own bunk over on that side? Very well, then, I'll take this. What a ripping little house this is! Everything so handy!"

He clambered into his bunk and rolled himself well up in the blankets, and slumber gathered him forthwith, as a swath of barley is folded into the arms of the reaping-machine.

The weary Mole also was glad to turn in without delay, and soon had his head on his pillow, in great joy and contentment. But ere he closed his eyes he let them wander round his old room, mellow in the glow of the firelight that played or rested on familiar and friendly things which had long been unconsciously a part of him, and now smilingly received him back, without rancour. He was now in just the frame of mind that the tactful Rat had quietly worked to bring about in him. He saw clearly how plain and simple—how narrow, even—it all was; but clearly, too, how much it all meant to him, and the special value of some such anchorage in one's existence. He did not at all want to abandon the new life and its splendid spaces, to turn his back on sun and air and all they offered him and creep home and stay there; the upper world was all too strong, it called to him still, even down there, and he knew he must return to the larger stage. But it was good to think he had this to come back to, this place which was all his own, these things which were so glad to see him again and could always be counted upon for the same simple welcome.

——Kenneth Grahame

Carol, Brothers, Carol

Carol, brothers carol,
Carol joyfully,
Carol the good tidings,
Carol merrily!
And pray a gladsome Christmas
For all good Christian men,
Carol, brothers, carol,
Christmas comes again.
                —*William A. Muhlenberg*

The Little Pagan Faun

IT WAS THE EVE of the second (or was it the third?) of all the Christmases when three little, rather self-esteeming, girl seraphs slipped out of the pearly gates of one of the heavenly spheres and ran merrily down the star-powdered stairways of the sky to sing carols to the Little Child. They were in fact the first of the waits, but they didn't know that they were.

When they got to the earth they found that they had made a slight miscalculation, and that they had still to go through a fir-wood before they came to the Babe's abode. Very beautiful the fir-wood looked in the frosty moonlight, and very beautiful the three little seraphs looked too as they hastened through it; while the faint and tender effulgence of their preparatory Paradise which was still about them made the pine-shadows deeper and

Reprinted by permission of the Proprietors of *Punch*.

more velvety and the three little seraphs themselves to look like three little glorified glow-worms.

Very lovely were their flower faces, you may be sure; and their best clothes, new on for the occasion, were all the scarlets, blues and golds that you can imagine. Their halcyon* wings too were folded closely about them and over their chests, for it was cold, and the snow and the moonlight were of course strange to them, and a little frightening besides, and so they ran tippity-tip-toe, each carrying her harp.

Now there sat in the wood on the stump of a tree a freckled little pagan faun; he was a very little one, and he was feeling uncommon lonesome, for his family had been a bit out of it for the last year or more; and so there he sat alone, and occasionally he blew himself a few notes on his whistle for company, and between whiles he blew on his fingers to keep them warm.

Presently he saw the three little seraphs running tippity-tip-toe, and he thought that he'd never seen anything so lovely before, and he longed to be their playmate.

"Oh, you lovely little girl nymphs," said he (for he knew no better), "where are you going to?"

"Oh, you little pagan faun," said the biggest one of the three little seraphs, "we are going to sing carols to the Babe."

"May I not come with you?" asked the little faun, ever so humbly; "I can't sing carols but I can play tunes on my whistle."

"No, indeed, you little pagan faun," replied the biggest one again, "certainly not"; and her two little sparkly

* Seraphs' wings, it has been stated, serve no practical purpose for flying with, their position in the shoulder being destructive to equilibrity if so used.

зisters said, "*What* an idea!" and they all ran on, more
tippety-tip-toe than ever, and came to the Babe's abode.

And then there they stood up, outside in the snow and
sang their carols more clearly and sweetly than thrushes.
And this is what they thought as they were singing:

The first one thought, "How beautifully I'm singing
tonight, and how pleased the Babe will be to hear me!"

The second one thought, "How sweetly I make my harp
to ring, and how happy the Babe must be listening to it!"

The third one thought, "How becoming to me are these
beautiful clothes I have put on in the Babe's honour, and
how he'll clap his hands to see me!"

Thus then they thought as they sang together more
clearly and sweetly than thrushes.

And in the sharp blue shadow of a pine-tree sat the little
faun, who had followed them there, far off and unbe-
knownst, and his heart was in his little pagan throat, for
never had he heard such tunes or seen such flower faces
in all the forest.

And when the carols were sung the biggest little seraph
went to the door and knocked, and the Lady of the House,
who was the Babe's mother, opened it and stood there
holding the Babe to her heart; and very sweet and kindly
she looked with the firelight about her and her little son
sitting, grave and sleepily grey-eyed, in her arms.

And the three little seraphs all curtseyed down to the
snow, very low indeed, and then they all said together,
"We wish you a merry Christmas and we hope you liked
our carols."

Now as a matter of fact the Lady and the Babe hadn't
heard the carols at all, not a note of 'em, though the singers
had sung them more clearly and sweetly than thrushes;
and this was, as the Lady knew at once and you will

probably guess, because the three little self-esteeming seraphs had thought all the time only of their own sweet singing, their own sweet harping and their lovely new clothes, and thus had rendered their music mute to those in whose honor it was intended.

But the Lady of the House was too kind and gentle to say this, for she hated to hurt anyone, and the seraphs were really rather little darlings after all and meant very well. So she said:

"Thank you kindly, my dears"; and to her little son she said, "Say thank you" and the Babe said "Thank you" (for he could just talk a little), and speaking very clearly, gravely and politely.

And then she gave each of the three a bit of the Babe's birthday cake, although it was a day too soon to cut it, and wished them a merry Christmas, and they ran off, tippity-tip-toe again, through the cold and moonlit wood, their halcyon wings folded over their chests, until they came to the purple stairway, up which they ran, twinkling like stars, as fast as they'd run down it.

And when they'd gone and the house door was shut again, the little faun trotted timidly out of the shadows and began to blow a little tune on his whistle all about the summer and the hills of sheep and the little woolly lambs; and as he played he thought to himself thus:

"That was the most beautiful little boy shepherd I have ever seen, but he looks very grave, and I should love to make him laugh, so I will try very hard indeed to play my best for him, though he will think it very poor stuff after the carols."

Now he hadn't played more than half his tune before the Lady came to the door of her own accord and said, "Oh, you funny little faun, please to come in out of the

cold and finish the pretty tune that you are so kindly playing to us in the kitchen, where we can hear it even better."

So the faun stamped the snow off his hooves and came
in and put his whistle to his lips and played his tune so
merrily that the Babe laughed with delight, like robins
singing; and the Lady laughed too, as gaily as a girl,
tapping her foot the while with the music.

And when he'd done she gave the little faun an extra
big bit of birthday cake, and he asked, "Please, my lady,
mayn't I stay here for always and make tunes for the
Babe to laugh at."

And the Lady said very gently, "No, my dear, that can't
be; you must go back to the wood and play your tunes
to the rabbits and the shepherds and the shadows of the
trees, and so help the world laugh and go round. But,"
she added, "you shall come and stay with the Babe and
me when the world's gone round often enough; and a
merry Christmas to you, my dear, and thank you."

Now you mayn't be able to believe that the Lady promised the little pagan faun anything of the sort, but I can
assure you that she did, and that he trotted off into the
woods again, munching his cake and feeling much comforted about things, just as the clocks were striking twelve
and it was Christmas Day.

——*Patrick R. Chalmers*

The Barn

"I am tired of this barn!" said the colt.
"And every day it snows.
Outside there's no grass any more
And icicles grow on my nose.
I am tired of hearing the cows
Breathing and talking together.
I am sick of these clucking hens,
I hate stables and winter weather!"

"Hush! little colt," said the mare
"And a story I will tell
Of a barn like this one of ours
And the wonders that there befell.
It was weather much like this
And the beasts stood as we stand now
In the warm good dark of the barn—
A horse and an ass and a cow."

"And sheep?" asked the colt. "Yes, sheep
And a pig and a goat and a hen.
All of the beasts of the barnyard,
The usual servants of men.
And into their midst came a lady
And she was as cold as death
But the animals leaned above her
And made her warm with their breath.

"The Barn" is from *Compass Rose,* by Elizabeth Coatsworth; copyright, 1929, by Coward-McCann, Inc.; reprinted by permission.

"There was her baby born
And laid to sleep in the hay
While music flooded the rafters
And the barn was as light as day.
And angels and kings and shepherds
Came to worship the Babe from afar,
But we looked at Him first of all creatures
By the bright strange light of a star!"
——*Elizabeth Coatsworth*

"EVERYWHERE, EVERYWHERE,

CHRISTMAS TONIGHT!"

How Far Is it to Bethlehem?

How far is it to Bethlehem?
   Not very far.
Shall we find the stable-room
   Lit by the star?

Can we see the little Child,
   Is He within?
If we lift the wooden latch
   May we go in?

May we stroke the creatures there,
   Ox, ass, or sheep?
May we peer like them and see
   Jesus asleep?

If we touch His tiny hand
   Will He awake?
Will He know we've come so far
   Just for His sake?

Great Kings have precious gifts,
   And we have nought;
Little smiles and little tears
   Are all we brought.

For all weary children
   Mary must weep.
Here, on His bed of straw,
   Sleep, children, sleep.

Reprinted by permission of the Executrix of the late Mrs. G. K. Chesterton.

God, in His Mother's arms,
  Babes in the byre,
Sleep, as they sleep who find
  Their heart's desire.
        ——*Frances A. Chesterton*

Mr. Edwards Meets Santa Claus

THE DAYS WERE SHORT and cold, the wind whistled sharply, but there was no snow. Cold rains were falling. Day after day the rain fell, pattering from the roof and pouring from the eaves.

Mary and Laura stayed close by the fire, sewing their nine patch-quilt blocks, or cutting paper dolls from scraps of wrapping-paper, and hearing the wet sound of the rain. Every night was so cold that they expected to see snow the next morning, but in the morning they saw only sad, wet grass.

They pressed their noses against the squares of glass in the windows that Pa had made, and they were glad they could see out. But they wished they could see snow.

Laura was anxious because Christmas was near, and Santa Claus and his reindeer could not travel without snow. Mary was afraid that, even if it snowed, Santa Claus could not find them, so far away in Indian territory.

When they asked Ma about this, she said she didn't know.

"What day is it?" they asked her, anxiously. "How many more days until Christmas?" And they counted off the days on their fingers, till there was only one more day left.

Rain was still falling that morning. There was not one crack in the gray sky. They felt almost sure there would be no Christmas. Still, they kept hoping.

Just before noon the light changed. The clouds broke and drifted apart, shining white in a clear blue sky. The sun shone, birds sang, and thousands of drops of water sparkled on the grasses. But when Ma opened the door to let in the fresh, cold air, they heard the creek roaring.

They had not thought about the creek. Now they knew they would have no Christmas, because Santa Claus could not cross that roaring creek.

Pa came in, bringing a fat turkey. If it weighed less than twenty pounds, he said, he'd eat it, feathers and all. He asked Laura, "How's that for a Christmas dinner? Think you can manage one of those drumsticks?"

She said, yes, she could. But she was sober. Then Mary asked him if the creek was going down, and he said it was still rising.

Ma said it was too bad. She hated to think of Mr. Edwards eating his bachelor cooking all alone on Christmas day. Mr. Edwards had been asked to eat Christmas dinner with them, but Pa shook his head and said a man would risk his neck, trying to cross that creek now.

"No," he said. "That current's too strong. We'll just have to make up our minds that Edwards won't be here tomorrow."

Of course that meant that Santa Claus could not come, either.

Laura Ingalls Wilder: copyright, 1935, by Laura Ingalls Wilder; reprinted by permission of Harper and Brothers.

Laura and Mary tried not to mind too much. They watched Ma dress the wild turkey, and it was a very fat turkey. They were lucky little girls to have a good house to live in, and a warm fire to sit by, and such a turkey for their Christmas dinner. Ma said so, and it was true. Ma said it was too bad that Santa Claus couldn't come this year, but that they were such good girls that he hadn't forgotten them; he would surely come next year.

Still, they were not happy.

After supper that night they washed their hands and faces, buttoned their red-flannel nightgowns, tied their night-cap strings, and soberly said their prayers. They lay down in bed and pulled the covers up. It did not seem at all like Christmas time.

Pa and Ma sat silent by the fire. After a while Ma asked why Pa didn't play the fiddle, and he said, "I don't seem to have the heart to, Caroline."

After a longer while, Ma suddenly stood up.

"I'm going to hang up your stockings, girls," she said. "Maybe something will happen."

Laura's heart jumped. But then she thought again of the creek and she knew nothing could happen.

Ma took one of Mary's clean stockings and one of Laura's, and she hung them from the mantel-shelf, on either side of the fireplace. Laura and Mary watched her over the edge of their bed-covers.

"Now go to sleep," Ma said, kissing them good night. "Morning will come quicker if you are asleep."

She sat down by the fire and Laura almost went to sleep. She woke up a little when she heard Pa say, "You've only made it worse, Caroline."

And she thought she heard Ma say: "No, Charles.

There's the white sugar." But perhaps she was dreaming.

Then she heard Jack growl savagely. The door-latch rattled and someone said, "Ingalls! Ingalls!" Pa was stirring up the fire, and when he opened the door Laura saw that it was morning. The outdoors was gray.

"Great fishhooks, Edwards! Come in, man! What's happened?" he exclaimed.

Laura saw the stocking limply dangling, and she scrooged her shut eyes into the pillow. She heard Pa piling wood on the fire, and she heard Mr. Edwards say he had carried his clothes on his head when he swam the creek. His teeth rattled and his voice shivered. He would be all right, he said, when he got warm.

"It was too big a risk, Edwards," Pa said. "We're glad you're here but that was too big a risk for a Christmas dinner."

"Your little ones ought to have a Christmas," Mr. Edwards replied. "No creek could stop me, after I fetched them their gifts from Independence."

Laura sat straight up in bed. "Did you see Santa Claus?" she shouted!

"I sure did," Mr. Edwards said.

"Where? When? What did he look like? What did he say? Did he really give you something for us?" Mary and Laura cried.

"Wait, wait a minute!" Mr. Edwards laughed. And Ma said she would put the presents in the stockings, as Santa Claus intended. She said they mustn't look.

Mr. Edwards came and sat on the floor by their bed, and he answered every question they asked him. They honestly tried not to look at Ma, and they didn't quite see what she was doing.

When he saw the creek rising, Mr. Edwards said, he had known that Santa Claus could not get across it. ("But you crossed it," Laura said. "Yes," said Mr. Edwards, "but Santa Claus is too old and fat. He couldn't make it, where a long, lean razor-back like me could do so.") And Mr. Edwards reasoned that if Santa Claus couldn't cross the creek, likely he would come no further south than Independence. Why should he come forty miles across the prairie, only to be turned back? Of course he wouldn't do that!

So Mr. Edwards had walked to Independence. ("In the rain?" Mary asked. Mr. Edwards said he wore his rubber coat.) And there, coming down the street in Independence, he had met Santa Claus. ("In the daytime?" Laura asked. She hadn't thought that anyone could see Santa Claus in the daytime. No, Mr. Edwards said; it was night, but light shone out across the street from the saloons.)

Well, the first thing that Santa Claus said was, "Hello, Edwards!" ("Did he know you?" Mary asked, and Laura asked, "How did you know he was really Santa Claus?" Mr. Edwards said that Santa Claus knew everybody. And he had recognized Santa at once by his whiskers. Santa Claus had the longest, thickest, whitest set of whiskers west of the Mississippi.)

So Santa Claus said, "Hello Edwards! Last time I saw you you were sleeping on a corn shuck bed in Tennessee." And Mr. Edwards well remembered the little pair of red-yarn mittens that Santa Claus had left for him that time.

Then Santa Claus said: "I understand you're living now down along the Verdigris River. Have you ever met up, down yonder, with two little girls named Mary and Laura?"

"I surely am acquainted with them," Mr. Edwards replied.

"It rests heavy on my mind," said Santa Claus. "They are both of them sweet, pretty, good little young things, and I know they are expecting me. I surely do hate to disappoint the good little girls like them. Yet with the water up the way it is, I can't ever make it across that creek. I can figure no way whatsoever to get to their cabin this year, Edwards," Santa Claus said. "Would you do me the favor to fetch their gifts this one time?"

"I'll do that, and with pleasure," Mr. Edwards told him.

Then Santa Claus and Mr. Edwards stepped across the street to the hitching-posts where the pack-mule was tied. ("Didn't he have his reindeer?" Laura asked. "You know he couldn't," Mary said. "There isn't any snow." "Exactly," said Mr. Edwards. Santa Claus travelled with a pack-mule in the southwest.)

And Santa Claus uncinched the pack and looked through it, and he took out the presents for Mary and Laura.

"Oh, what are they?" Laura cried; but Mary asked, "Then what did he do?"

Then he shook hands with Mr. Edwards, and he swung up on his fine bay horse. Santa Claus rode well for a man of his weight and build. And he tucked his long, white wiskers under his bandana. "So long, Edwards," he said, and he rode away on the Fort Dodge trail, leading his pack mule and whistling.

Laura and Mary were silent an instant, thinking of that. Then Ma said, "You may look now, girls."

Something was shining bright in the top of Laura's stocking. She squealed and jumped out of bed. So did Mary, but Laura beat her to the fireplace. And the shining thing was a glittering new tin cup.

Mary had one just like it.

These new tin cups were their very own. Now they each had a cup to drink out of. Laura jumped up and down and shouted and laughed but Mary stood still and looked with shining eyes at her own tin cup.

Then they plunged their hands into the stockings again. And they pulled out two long, long sticks of candy. It was peppermint candy, striped red and white. They looked and looked at that beautiful candy, and Laura licked her stick, just one lick. But Mary was not so greedy. She didn't even take one lick at her stick.

Those stockings weren't empty yet. Mary and Laura pulled out two small packages. They unwrapped them, and each found a little heart-shaped cake. Over their delicate brown tops was sprinkled white sugar. The sparkling grains lay like tiny drifts of snow.

The cakes were too pretty to eat. Mary and Laura just looked at them. But at last Laura turned hers over, and she nibbled a tiny nibble from underneath, where it wouldn't show. And the inside of that little cake was white!

It has been made of pure white flour, and sweetened with white sugar.

Laura and Mary never would have looked in their stockings again. The cups and the cakes and the candy were almost too much. They were too happy to speak.

But Ma asked if they were sure the stockings were empty.

Then they put their arms down inside them, to make sure.

And in the toe of each stocking was a shining bright, new penny!

They had never even thought of such a thing as having a penny. Think of having a whole penny for your very own. Think of having a cup and a cake and a stick of candy *and* a penny.

There never had been such a Christmas.

Now of course, right away, Laura and Mary should have thanked Mr. Edwards for bringing those lovely presents all the way from Independence. But they had forgotten all about Mr. Edwards. They had even forgotten Santa Claus. In a minute they would have remembered, but before they did, Ma said, gently, "Aren't you going to thank Mr. Edwards?"

"Oh, thank you, Mr. Edwards! Thank you!" they said, and they meant it with all their hearts. Pa shook Mr. Edwards' hand, too, and they shook it again. Pa and Ma and Mr. Edwards acted as if they were almost crying, Laura didn't know why. So she gazed again at her beautiful presents.

She looked up again when Ma gasped. And Mr. Edwards was taking sweet potatoes out of his pockets. He said they had helped to balance the package on his head when he swam across the creek. He thought Pa and Ma might like them, with the Christmas turkey.

There were nine sweet potatoes. Mr. Edwards had brought them all the way from town, too. It was just too much. Pa said so. "It's too much, Edwards," he said. They never could thank him enough.

Mary and Laura were much too excited to eat breakfast. They drank the milk from their shining new cups, but they could not swallow the rabbit stew and the cornmeal mush.

"Don't make them, Charles," Ma said. "It will soon be dinner time."

For Christmas dinner there was the tender, juicy, roasted turkey. There were the sweet potatoes, baked in the ashes and carefully wiped so that you could eat the good skins, too. There was a loaf of salt-rising bread made from the last of the white flour.

And after all that there were stewed dried blackberries and little cakes. But these little cakes were made with brown sugar and they did not have white sugar sprinkled over their tops.

Then Pa and Ma and Mr. Edwards sat by the fire and talked about Christmas times back in Tennessee and up north in the Big Woods. But Mary and Laura looked at their beautiful cakes and played with their pennies and drank water out of their new cups. And little by little they licked and sucked their sticks of candy, till each stick was sharp-pointed on one end.

That was a happy Christmas.

——Laura Ingalls Wilder

An Old Christmas Greeting

Sing Hey! Sing Hey!
For Christmas Day,
Twine mistletoe and holly;
For friendship grows
In winter snows,
And so let's all be jolly.

——Nursery Rhyme

The Peterkins' Christmas-Tree

EARLY IN THE AUTUMN the Peterkins began to
prepare for their Christmas-tree. Everything was done
in great privacy, as it was to be a surprise to the neighbors,
as well as to the rest of the family. Mr. Peterkin had been
up to Mr. Bromwick's wood-lot, and, with his consent,
selected the tree. Agamemnon went to look at it occasionally after dark, and Solomon John made frequent visits
to it mornings, just after sunrise. Mr. Peterkin drove
Elizabeth Eliza and her mother that way, and pointed
furtively to it with his whip; but none of them ever spoke
of it aloud to each other. It was suspected that the little
boys had been to see it Wednesday and Saturday after-
noons. But they came home with their pockets full of
chestnuts, and said nothing about it. At length Mr. Peterkin had it cut down and brought secretly into the Larkin's
barn. A week or two before Christmas a measurement was

made of it with Elizabeth Eliza's yard-measure. To Mr. Peterkin's great dismay it was discovered that it was too high to stand in the back parlor.

This fact was brought out at a secret council of Mr. and Mrs. Peterkin, Elizabeth Eliza, and Agamemnon.

Agamemnon suggested that it might be set up slanting; but Mrs. Peterkin was very sure it would make her dizzy, and the candles would drip.

But a brilliant idea came to Mr. Peterkin. He proposed that the ceiling of the parlor should be raised to make room for the top of the tree.

Elizabeth Eliza thought the space would need to be quite large. It must not be like a small box, or you could not see the tree.

"Yes," said Mr. Peterkin, "I should have the ceiling lifted all across the room; the effect would be finer."

Elizabeth Eliza objected to having the whole ceiling raised, because her room was over the back parlor, and she would have no floor while the alteration was going on, which would be very awkward. Besides, her room was not very high now, and, if the floor were raised, perhaps she could not walk in it upright.

Mr. Peterkin explained that he didn't propose altering the whole ceiling, but to lift up a ridge across the room at the back part where the tree was to stand. This would make a hump, to be sure, in Elizabeth Eliza's room; but it would go across the whole room.

Elizabeth Eliza said she would not mind that. It would be like the cuddy thing that comes up on the deck of a ship, that you sit against, only here you would not have the sea-sickness. She thought she should like it, for a rarity. She might use it for a divan.

Mrs. Peterkin thought it would come in the worn place of the carpet, and might be a convenience in making the carpet over.

Agamemnon was afraid there would be trouble in keeping the matter secret, for it would be a long piece of work for a carpenter; but Mr. Peterkin proposed having the carpenter for a day or two, for a number of other jobs.

One of them was to make all the chairs in the house of the same height, for Mrs. Peterkin had nearly broken her spine by sitting down in a chair that she had supposed was her own rocking-chair, and it had proved to be two inches lower. The little boys were now large enough to sit in any chair; so a medium was fixed upon to satisfy all the family, and the chairs were made uniformly of the same height.

On consulting the carpenter, however, he insisted that the tree could be cut off at the lower end to suit the height of the parlor, and demurred at so great a change as altering the ceiling. But Mr. Peterkin had set his mind upon the improvement, and Elizabeth Eliza had cut her carpet in preparation for it.

So the folding-doors into the back parlor were closed, and for nearly a fortnight before Christmas there was great litter of fallen plastering, and laths, and chips, and shavings; and Elizabeth Eliza's carpet was taken up, and the furniture had to be changed, and one night she had to sleep at the Bromwicks', for there was a long hole in her floor that might be dangerous.

All this delighted the little boys. They could not understand what was going on. Perhaps they suspected a Christmas-tree, but they did not know why a Christmas-tree should have so many chips, and were still more astonished at the hump that appeared in Elizabeth Eliza's room. It must be a Christmas present, or else the tree in a box.

Some aunts and uncles, too, arrived a day or two before Christmas, with some small cousins. These cousins occupied the attention of the little boys, and there was a great deal of whispering and mystery, behind doors, and under the stairs, and in the corners of the entry.

Solomon John was busy, privately making some candles for the tree. He had been collecting some bayberries, as he understood they made very nice candles, so that it would not be necessary to buy any.

The elders of the family never all went into the back parlor together, and all tried not to see what was going on. Mrs. Peterkin would go in with Solomon John, or Mr. Peterkin with Elizabeth Eliza, or Elizabeth Eliza and Agamemnon and Solomon John. The little boys and the small cousins were never allowed even to look inside the room.

Elizabeth Eliza meanwhile went into town a number of times. She wanted to consult Amanda as to how much ice-cream they should need, and whether they could make it at home, as they had cream and ice. She was pretty busy in her own room; the furniture had to be changed, and the carpet altered. The "hump" was higher than she expected. There was danger of bumping her own head whenever she crossed it. She had to nail some padding on the ceiling for fear of accidents.

The afternoon before Christmas, Elizabeth Eliza, Solomon John, and their father collected in the back parlor for a council. The carpenters had done their work, and the tree stood at its full height at the back of the room, the top stretching up into the space arranged for it. All the chips and shavings were cleared away, and it stood on a neat box.

But what were they to put upon the tree?

Solomon John had brought in his supply of candles; but they proved to be very "stringy" and very few of them. It was strange how many bayberries it took to make a few candles! The little boys had helped him, and he had gathered as much as a bushel of bayberries. He had put them in water, and skimmed off the wax, according to the directions; but there was so little wax!

Solomon John had given the little boys some of the bits sawed off from the legs of the chairs. He had suggested that they should cover them with gilt paper, to answer for gilt apples, without telling them what they were for. These apples, a little blunt at the end, and the candles were all they had for the tree!

After all her trips into town Elizabeth Eliza had forgotten to bring anything for it.

"I thought of candies and sugar-plums," she said; "but I concluded if we made caramels ourselves we should not need them. But, then, we have not made caramels. The fact is, that day my head was full of my carpet. I had bumped it pretty badly, too."

Mr. Peterkin wished he had taken, instead of a fir tree, an apple-tree he had seen in October, full of red fruit.

"But the leaves would have fallen off by this time," said Elizabeth Eliza.

"And the apples, too," said Solomon John.

"It is odd I should have forgotten, that day I went in on purpose to get the things," said Elizabeth Eliza, musingly.

"But I went from shop to shop, and didn't know exactly what to get. I saw a great many gilt things for Christmas-trees; but I knew the little boys were making the gilt apples; there were plenty of candles in the shops, but I knew Solomon John was making the candles."

Mr. Peterkin thought it was quite natural.

Solomon John wondered if it were too late for them to go into town now.

Elizabeth Eliza could not go in the next morning, for there was to be a grand Christmas dinner, and Mr. Peterkin could not be spared, and Solomon John was sure he and Agamemnon would not know what to buy. Besides, they would want to try the candles to-night.

Mr. Peterkin asked if the presents everybody had been preparing would not answer. But Elizabeth Eliza knew they would be too heavy.

A gloom came over the room. There was only a flickering gleam from one of Solomon John's candles that he had lighted by way of trial.

Solomon John again proposed going into town. He lighted a match to examine the newspaper about the trains. There were plenty of trains coming out at that hour, but none going in except a very late one. That would not leave time to do anything and come back.

"We could go in, Elizabeth Eliza and I," said Solomon John, "but we should not have time to buy anything."

Agamemnon was summoned in. Mrs. Peterkin was entertaining the uncles and aunts in the front parlor. Agamemnon wished there was time to study up something about electric lights. If they could only have a calcium light! Solomon John's candle sputtered and went out.

At this moment there was a loud knocking at the front

door. The little boys, and the small cousins, and the uncles and aunts, and Mrs. Peterkin, hastened to see what was the matter.

The uncles and aunts thought somebody's house must be on fire. The door was opened, and there was a man, white with flakes, for it was beginning to snow, and he was pulling in a large box.

Mrs. Peterkin supposed it contained some of Elizabeth Eliza's purchases, so she ordered it to be pushed into the back parlor, and hastily called back her guests and the little boys into the other room. The little boys and the small cousins were sure they had seen Santa Claus himself.

Mr. Peterkin lighted the gas. The box was addressed to Elizabeth Eliza. It was from the lady from Philadelphia! She had gathered a hint from Elizabeth Eliza's letters that there was to be a Christmas-tree, and had filled this box with all that would be needed.

It was opened directly. There was every kind of gilt hanging-thing, from gilt pea-pods to butterflies on springs. There were shining flags and lanterns, and birdcages, and nests with birds sitting on them, baskets of fruit, gilt apples and bunches of grapes, and, at the bottom of the whole, a large box of candles and a box of Philadelphia bonbons!

Elizabeth Eliza and Solomon John could scarcely keep from screaming. The little boys and the small cousins knocked on the folding-doors to ask what was the matter.

Hastily Mr. Peterkin and the rest took out the things and hung them on the tree, and put on the candles.

When all was done, it looked so well that Mr. Peterkin exclaimed:

"Let us light the candles now, and send to invite all the

neighbors to-night, and have the tree on Christmas Eve!"

And so it was that the Peterkins had their Christmas-tree the day before, and on Christmas night could go and visit their neighbors.

———*Lucretia Hale*

Christmas

JANCSI HAD HIS WISH. All night it snowed and for
a week afterwards, steadily. Drifts reached the windows,
covered gates and fences, made the road impassable. Every
morning and night the men had to shovel new paths from
the house to the out-buildings. Soon the paths were like
deep canyons between walls of snow. By the time it
stopped snowing, the walls were so high Jancsi completely disappeared between them.

With Uncle Sándor and the shepherds to help him,
there was very little for Father to do. One morning he
brought in his woodworking tools. "We need some new
chairs, Mother," he said. Jancsi helped him find well-

seasoned, dry maple planks in the woodshed. Uncle Sándor shook his head and smiled. "So you still make your own furniture! I don't see how you have patience for it when you can buy furniture so cheaply now."

Father grunted. "Glued and nailed factory rubbish! I want furniture we can *use,* not rickety stuff like that. Besides, I have nothing else to do now, shall I twiddle my thumbs and look at the snow?" He measured and cut out seats and backs, rungs and legs, for future chairs.

Uncle Sándor looked on for a while. Then he grew restless. Suddenly he exclaimed: "I haven't had an honest tool in my hands since I left for the city. Got a spare saw, Brother?"

Father laughed. "I knew you couldn't resist it, Sándor, there isn't a man who can resist the song of the saw."

Soon Uncle Sándor was working, humming and whistling to himself. Evenings, the shepherds helped, too. One by one the rough pieces were planed and whittled, smoothed and rubbed down. Leisurely, carefully, painstakingly, they worked until each piece fitted the other perfectly. Then they were fastened together with wooden dowels.

Father threw himself on the first complete chair with all his weight. "Built for a lifetime!" he exclaimed with satisfaction.

Mother was teaching Kate to spin. In the fall, a little after harvest time, she had prepared the flax. Kate told her father how it was done. "We soaked it first, Daddy, soaked it in big tubs for two days. Then dried it in the sun. Later on Auntie showed me how to break the hard fibers in the flax. She has a machine—it works like a clothes wringer, only you don't roll the flax in it, but work it up and down like scissors. Then we tied the flax in sheaves and combed it out with a wire comb to make it all smooth and even. Here it is, Daddy, on the spinning wheel. See, I can make a nice long thread!" She could, too; the thread she made was just as thin and even as Mother's.

Uncle Sándor looked at Mother. "What have you done to the child, my dear? I sent a spoiled, cranky, pale little girl to you. I find a husky, happy, busy little farmer. She will never fit into city life again!"

Kate stopped the spinning wheel and sat in his lap. "Daddy, I don't want to go back to the city. Can't we just stay here for good? Please!"

"But, Kate. Your education—my work . . ." Uncle Sándor turned to Father, who was looking at them gravely. "What future would she have here, without schools, miles away from civilization?"

Father smiled. "You are a schoolteacher, aren't you, Brother? Well, here is Kate, here is Jancsi, here are these young shepherds, eager to learn. The schoolmaster in the village is so old he can't really teach any more. You could take his place. Wouldn't it be beautiful if you could bring learning and civilization to all these people? Your own people?"

Pista was listening to all this with much interest. Now he spoke. "Don't take the little lady away from us, Mister Nagy. Stay here with her. You are earning money with your work now, I know. Here, you wouldn't be paid in money—you would earn love and peace and happiness!"

Kate slipped off her father's lap. Her face was shining.

She was standing in the middle of the room straight as an arrow. "You remember what you told us, Pista, when I first saw you? I remember every word of it. Listen, Daddy, 'The sky gives me sunshine and rain. The ground gives me food and water. The sheep give me clothing and my bed. The beautiful flowers and animals show me what to carve with my knife. Can money and schools give me more?' That's what he said, Daddy. He gave me this necklace."

"And you showed me how to write my name," interrupted Pista.

"That's how Kate's school started," laughed Father.

"Kate's school? What's that?" asked Uncle Sándor.

"Oh, we never told you about it, Brother, did we? Since you have been here the lessons stopped, the boys didn't want to disturb your visit. Kate has taught Jancsi and the shepherds to read and write. Made a good job of it, too!" said Father proudly.

Uncle Sándor was speechless. He looked from one to the other. Then he began to walk up and down, deep in thought. They watched him anxiously. Minutes passed. He stopped and looked at Father.

"I don't know what to do. Give me a week to think it over, Brother Márton."

"A week? You will have half the winter to think it over. Mountains of snow don't melt in a week," laughed Father. "But that reminds me, Christmas Eve is a week from tonight. Where will we get a Christmas tree?"

This was a puzzle. It was impossible even to attempt a drive to the mountains where the pine trees grew.

"We'll have to do without one, but it won't feel like Christmas," said Mother sadly.

"I could *make* one," proposed Pista.

They thought he was joking; how could anyone *make* a Christmas tree?

"I'll tell you how. I will carve out the trunk and branches—then we can dye some straw green, cut it into small pieces, and glue them on the branches."

"Or we could paint paper green and cut it into long narrow strips with frilled edges," cried Kate.

"And we can trim it with popcorn. I'll make some small cookies and we can tie those on, too," said Mother eagerly.

Everybody had a new idea. "I am glad we can't get a real tree—this will be much more fun," said Jancsi.

Next day Pista had his tree ready. They pasted strips of green paper on the branches, and some colored straw, too. Kate and Jancsi made long strings of popcorn. Mother gave them strawberry juice from her preserves and they dipped part of the corn into that and had red and white strings. Mother made cookies and she polished small apples. They would go on the tree, too.

Father fitted the tree into a high stand he carved. Uncle Sándor cut little angels and intricate chains out of colored paper. Everybody helped to make it beautiful. Long candles were cut into short pieces and fastened on the tree with wires. The day before Christmas, Mother and Kate trimmed it. "It's more beautiful than any tree I ever saw in the city," cried Uncle Sándor when it was finished.

Mother, of course, found time to cook and bake and roast a wonderful supper. Kate set a real holiday table with the best pottery, a snow-white tablecloth, blazing candles, and a big bowl of red apples for the centerpiece. All the shepherds were invited for the evening.

Darkness fell early. It was Christmas Eve. When everything was ready, Jancsi went out to call the shepherds. In a little while they came, led by the oldest of them. He brought a gift. It was a small scene of Bethlehem, all carved of wood. The Christ Child in a tiny manger filled with straw, Mary and Joseph, the angels, the shepherds, the three wise men, the oxen, and the donkeys were all there. He set it under the tree tenderly and turned around. "Blessed be the house of our good master and everybody in it," he said.

Father shook hands with him. "Thank you, and God bless every one of you, my boys. Sit down now—supper is ready."

It was a merry meal. Kate's father kept the shepherds spellbound as he described the electric lights, automobiles, telephones, radio—the life in the city. They listened eagerly, like children to a fairytale. After supper, Father lighted the candles on the tree. He put out all the others on the table. Then he opened the door wide. "Welcome, Christ Child," he said. Through the open door, across the silent fields, came the faint but crystal-clear voice of the village church bells.

Uncle Sándor stepped to the door. "Silent night, holy night," he said softly. Kate's clear little voice rose, singing "Silent Night, Holy Night"; then Mother took up the tune, then all of them were singing it.

When the song was ended, they sat around the blazing stove, leaving the door open. Outside it had stopped snowing, and the sky was glittering with silvery stars. For a little while everybody was silent, there was utter peace and contentment in the room. Now and then the plaintive cry of lambs came from the sheepfolds, or a cow would moo softly in the barn.

"Next week, if you can spare some wood, Mister Nagy, I'd like to make new feeding racks. We have more sheep this year than ever before. They are crowded," said Pista.

Father nodded. "There is plenty of wood in the shed. I'll help you."

"One of you will have to carve a new bobbin for my weaving-frame. Kate and I will start to make linen next week," mused Mother. "And put in more flax next year, Father; my sheets are wearing out."

"I'd like to make a nice tablecloth too—with red hearts and white doves all around the edge!" sighed Kate.

"That pattern takes a very long time, Kate; we have only one frame."

"We could build another one for the little lady," spoke Pista.

"I'd like to build one for her," said Uncle Sándor. "Remember the one you and I made for our mother, Márton?"

Father turned his head slowly and looked at him. "That took a long time to make, Brother. We worked on it for months and months—maybe a year."

Uncle Sándor smiled. "I know. Maybe a year, maybe more. Every little piece carved and polished. That's the kind I'll build for Kate."

"May I help you, Uncle Sándor?" asked Jancsi.

"Of course, Jancsi and I can have it ready for you Kate—we can have it ready for next Christmas."

Kate, who was curled up in his lap, giggled. "Please say that again, Daddy. Say it very loud, so we can all hear you!"

"I said, we can have it ready for next—" Uncle Sándor stopped and looked at Father, who was laughing too. "Yes —yes, Sándor, go on!"

Kate sighed and snuggled down contentedly. "You don't have to *shout,* Daddy, we knew it all the time."

"Knew what, you little imp?"

"That you'll stay home—with us!"

—*Kate Seredy*

For Christmas

Now not a window small or big
But wears a wreath of holly sprig;
Nor any shop too poor to show
Its spray of pine or mistletoe.
Now city airs are spicy-sweet
With Christmas trees along each street,
Green spruce and fir whose boughs still hold
Their tinsel balls and fruits of gold.
Now postmen pass in threes or fours
Like bent, blue-coated Santa Claus.
Now people hurry to and fro
With little girls and boys in tow,
And not a child but keeps some trace
Of Christmas secrets in his face.

——*Rachel Field*

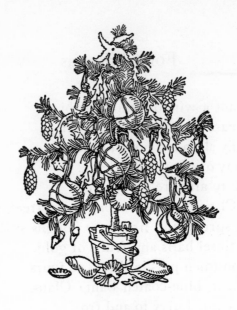

December

FATHER LOVED SURPRISES.

This year Christmas came on Friday, and Thursday morning he said to Cousin Mary and the children at breakfast, "We're leaving at ten. Get your suitcases packed for four days, and if you happen to have any pies or cake in the house you might bring them along. I'll pack a basket with supplies."

Four faces looked at him while four spoons hung forgotten in the air.

"Why, what do you mean?" asked Cousin Mary. "Ten o'clock tomorrow?"

"No, no, Cousin Mary. Father means ten o'clock today!" cried Jean, leaping from her chair to run around the table to hug her father. "It's today! Oh, where are we going?"

"Don't strangle me," said Father calmly, "and your porridge has to be eaten, you know, before you can go exploring. No, Lydia, there are no horses in this. And you'll all know where we are going when we get there."

Mark understood what was being said, but he was chiefly interested in one thing.

"Pie?" he repeated, like a little parrot. "Cake? I'll finish the pie."

"That's for the adventure, ducky," cried Jean gaily, finishing her porridge and banana much too fast. "Cousin Mary, may I please be excused? I have all the presents for the family to pack, too."

Cousin Mary protested a little more about so sudden a plan. She was accustomed to thinking about a plan until she was well used to it before she started to act on it. Even her new dresses were hung in her closet a month or two, until they seemed familiar, before she could bring herself to wear them. But since the children and now their father had come to live with her, she was really beginning to enjoy the excitement of doing things on the spur of the minute.

Still, when the children had thundered upstairs to make their beds and begin their packing, she said to their father, "Now that the children are gone, you can tell me where we are going."

But, no, he wouldn't tell. His eyes danced mischievously.

"It's to be a surprise for you all," he said. "You, most of all," and he began rummaging in the pantry and putting things like sugar and salt and flour in small tins and stowing them away in baskets to take with them.

By ten o'clock they were all ready. Everyone had begun by trying to bring too much; but in the end they had put most of the things back where they came from, and even then the luggage trunk at the back of the car, and the space at their feet, too, were pretty well filled. But no one minded that. At the last moment Cousin Mary remembered that she had forgotten about the hens, and jumped out of the front seat and hurried off to ask her next-door neighbor—who had hens of her own—if she would feed Cousin Mary's, too, for a few days.

Then they started off. They didn't turn down town but off to the highway past the old grain mill; beside the harbor, which looked gray under the gray sky; up old Colony Hill.

It was not a very cold day, and not a very pretty day, either. The sky was covered with clouds, and yet they didn't promise snow. Now and then the sun would glint through for a little and a silver gleam would appear on the gray water, and a pale glow strike across the withered grass and the leafless trees.

"It's not Christmas weather at all!" cried Lydia. "How can the Christ Child be born without a carpet of snow to spread about his stable, and a curtain of snow for the angels to fly through?"

Jean did not imagine Christmas Eve that way.

"It was hot, Lydia," she said. "There were palm trees, and the camels stood about and the shepherds wore sandals without any stockings. There wasn't any snow. The star shone down through the hot warm night—like that time last July when we didn't even put our sheets over us. Isn't that true, Father?"

"Well," said Father, "neither was true. I had a friend who was in Jerusalem one Christmas and he said it was gray, with an icy wind and the dust blowing. There wasn't any snow, but he said he had never been colder in his life. There were camels on the hills, looking miserable, with their backs to the wind. And I guess the shepherds wore sandals, but they crouched behind the rocks and shivered over their little fires."

"*Our* Christmases," said Lydia with decision, "should be the way I've described. White and bright, and then the blue sky coming out; and every footprint should be new like the first footprint in the world, made by the first man . . . and the first mouse and the first rabbit and the first deer—"

"And the first everything," Jean summed up. "Father, where are we going?"

But Father only shook his head. They were going south, that much they could see.

"Plymouth?" coaxed Lydia, breathing down Father's neck. "Is it Plymouth?"

But Father shook his head.

"I won't tell."

Just before they came to the great bridge which crosses the Cape Cod Canal they got out for an early lunch, which only Mark and his father did justice to—the others were too excited to eat much. And then they drove on. Now they were on the cape, passing through pretty villages with white cottages and big elms and now and then seeing, across the distant dunes, the glint of the bay.

Still they drove on. At Orleans, Father got out to go into a grocery for final supplies.

As they waited in the car Jean said, "It's as though we were starting on a pirate cruise. Hush, Mark! Stop humming! I hear the waves breaking."

Now as they drove they caught glimpses of the sea—

not the bay, as they had before, but the sea breaking in slow curlings of silver on miles of beaches, with dunes which they could see across the marshes.

Suddenly Father turned off on a side road and the car was heading straight out toward the ocean itself. They were on a bluff. The sea below them looked enormous. There were no headlands, no Milnot's light on its rocks, not even a ship. Only the sea gulls cried over the waves, and the little shore larks flew twittering over the harsh dune grass in the wind. There was a big white building behind them with a lookout on the roof.

"It's the Nauset Coast Guard Station. You'll see one of the men on the lookout now," said Father, but he drove on between the dunes and the marshes.

Unless one has driven on a dune road it would be hard to think of how it would twist and wind, now hard and smooth, now deep in the sand almost to the hubs of the car's wheels. In the bad places the road split into three or four roads. It wasn't easy to see which was the best, when all were bad. Cousin Mary held on tight and fixed her eyes far ahead. Yet, though they had to get out once or twice to push and put the boards under the tires, they arrived safely at the brown camp.

It was a shuttered building in the shelter of a high dune, with the grasses and lagoons of the marshes at its door and, far beyond, the pleasant uplands and the scattered white houses of Eastham. The roar of the waves shook the air. It was less cold here than in Hingham, but still it was gray with that waiting air.

"Here we are," said Father as they all sat rather breathlessly taking in their surroundings. "It belongs to Mr.

Danvers at my office, and he suggested we might like to use it."

Father had taken from his pocket a Yale key fastened to a smooth little piece of driftwood.

"Just right," Jean thought.

He opened the door while the family waited in silence close behind him. It seemed dark and damp and musty inside, but Father hurried about opening the shutters. Jean, as eldest, was allowed to light the fire left all ready in the fireplace and, with that on the hearth and the light coming in the windows, the place began to look pleasanter. There was a big room with a fireplace at one end with chairs about it. Along one wall was a table with an oil lamp on it, and at the other end was a wood stove with scarlet saucepans hanging behind it on the brown wall. Cousin Mary began carrying blankets out from the bedrooms and spreading them on the beach-plum bushes to dry, and the children dragged in suitcases and groceries from the car.

Soon the place began to look as if it were theirs. Cousin Mary made hot chocolate, the little girls buttered rolls, and they sat down to a house-warming party.

But behind the dunes was the sea, endlessly bringing up its waves to tower like walls of glass and then hurl themselves down along the sands in long scallops edged with lace. Above the white scallops of the waves there ran a brown scallop of driftwood and seaweed, marking high tide. After running races and skipping stones and mocking the sea gulls along the lonely beach, the family turned toward Nauset Station a mile away.

The sea was beautiful and wild and wonderful, but

before very long all five were walking along the high-tide mark. It was very fascinating—the ocean's wastebasket, where it had spilled all the things it didn't want. There were pink crab shells, and grapefruit rinds and electric light bulbs (never broken) and bottles and kelp and sea gull feathers and mysterious bits of cloth, and painted markers for lobster pots and skeletons of fish. All at once Jean and Lydia gave a cry together and raced toward something which they saw ahead of them, lying like a great green fairy bubble among the seaweed. It was a ball of glass such as fishermen sometimes use for their nets or as buoys for their lobster-pots. It was the color of a wave, beautiful and unbroken.

Jean reached it first and scooped it up while Lydia watched her, panting.

"It's the most beautiful thing I ever saw," Lydia said bravely.

Jean came to a sudden decision.

"You may have it," she said.

Her gesture as she gave it to the astonished Lydia was a little grand, like a princess.

"Oh, Jean!" Lydia faltered.

The green glass ball was as close to magic as she had ever come.

"I don't want it," Jean said, beginning to skip away.

But the sea must appreciate generosity.

"What's that?" Cousin Mary asked suddenly. "Out there in the water?"

It was another glass ball, and a third one was already being played with in the froth along the beach. It took some time before the waves were willing to let the children have their treasures. They flung balls down at their feet and then hastily hauled them back down the shore and pounced noisily upon them again, only to throw them again to the children and then once more to change their minds. But in the end the sea gave them its present. Each child had a gift from the ocean, a little early for Christmas but not too early for their plans.

"That gives me an idea," said Father. "I'll borrow an ax at the station and cut down a little pine at the edge of the woods; and you children can trim it for a sea Christmas tree, with the three glass balls, first of all, and then anything else we can find along the beach—we've plenty of string."

The pink and lavender shells were, of course, pretty. The family chose only perfect ones. Then some of the seaweeds were nice, with colored stones held in their roots. They found several little bottles, too, which they filled with small pure-white pebbles kept shiny with sea water. Some one had the idea of fraying out an old rope to twist about the boughs like tinsel.

At the station several of the young men volunteered to come and help cut down the little pitch pine. As they walked up the sandy road they found bunches of gray bayberries to add to their skirtfuls, and cones from the larger of the little pitch pines which grew not far from the shore. Mark was beginning to tire, and a nice red-haired Coast Guardsman with freckles picked him up and carried him pick-a-pack. Another took a firm hold on the newly cut tree.

"We don't often have company on the beach at Christmas," they said. "We're off duty. You let us help."

As they passed the station the cook came running out with hot doughnuts in a bag.

"I'm no hand as a cook," he explained to Cousin Mary, "but perhaps these won't sink the ship."

And as he went back to his kitchen, they all called out, "Merry Christmas!"

The short way down the bluff to the beach was by a rough flight of stairs built along the face of the sand. For some reason the dunes here had shelved off and seemed to be made of black earth instead of sand. There were various black humps and bumps in the earth. Father spoke of them to the young men.

"They say that's peat. There used to be a cedar swamp here, a good many thousands of years ago, I've heard people say who study that kind of thing."

"It's at least twenty feet deep and with feet of sand on top of that, so the swamp must have been there a long time ago," Father said. "Would any of those logs burn?"

"Never thought of trying," the red-haired boy who was carrying Mark declared. "Why don't we dig one out?"

"A Christmas log that was a tree before the time of Christ," Jean murmured.

"A good deal before then," Father said.

He had laid down the basket and was helping to chop and pull and tug out a big log of wood. It was all black, almost as though it had turned to earth, but it had kept its shape. You could still see that it had once been a trunk with branches, too—something which had grown here when the shore had not been here at all, and when land creatures had roamed and hunted where the waves now broke.

They were tired that night and went to bed early, Cousin Mary and Jean and Lydia in the bunks in one room, Father and Mark in another.

Once Jean woke up and listened for a while to the splendid roar of the waves, but the next time she woke it was to hear Lydia's voice near to the window.

"It's snowed! It's snowed! And Christ has been born into an ermine world!"

Jean ran to the window. Snow had come in the night, and the sun had followed it. The sky was bright, clear blue above the white dunes, and the sea gulls overhead were blindingly white. A smell of cooking came from the next room.

They rushed out, calling, "Merry Christmas! Merry Christmas, everyone!"

There hung their stockings lumpy and exciting looking; there stood the little pine tree covered with sea things and glass balls and shore berries like a mermaid's plaything, and the black log lay at the back of the freshly arranged fire.

"It's a Christmas log from the old days. If it burns we shall have good luck for a year. If it doesn't burn we shan't," declared Jean. "May Lydia and I light it at the same moment? We must kneel down on the hearth and light it together."

"Me, too," said Mark, appearing tousled and half asleep in the door of his room.

Lydia smiled.

"Come here, ducky. I'll see that you don't burn your fingers."

While Father and Cousin Mary watched, the three children lighted the Christmas fire together and then sat back on their heels to look at it. Their lumpy Christmas stockings lay beside them, for a moment forgotten. The fire had caught the paper; its tongues shot up red among the driftwood. But the black Yule log—would that burn and bring them a happy year?

Now the flames were all about the ancient cedar, and yet it lay there as though made of iron. There was only the flapping sound of the fire, and the grumble of the sea on the beaches. And then it happened. The primeval log began to burn with a mane of small blue flames. The blue flames lengthened and turned yellow. The Yule log was burning. The year to come would be happy as this one had been.

"Merry Christmas!" they all called to one another again, turning to their presents—all but Mark, whose mouth was too full to say anything.

"You've eaten the candy cane from the top of the stocking!" accused Jean.

"You're a bad boy," Lydia said absent-mindedly, reaching for her stocking. Then she gave a groan. "You've eaten mine too!" she cried. "You're a very bad boy, Mark!"

"He's eaten mine, too," added Jean. "You're a very, very bad boy."

Mark licked his fingers in a business like way and began to dig into his little stocking like a terrier.

Christmas day had begun. Wonderful things were *always* beginning!

——*Elizabeth Coatsworth*

Carol for a New Zealand Child

Christmas in the picture book
Gold and white with snow
Winter in the desert
Where the three Kings go.
Ice on the camel-rein,
Rime on the crown,
Snow round the stable doors
Of Bethelem town.

I carol Baby Jesus
On a nor-west day,
A summer wind is blowing
Across the beach and bay.
Sea gulls whirl where
Children run to swim,
Laughter in the breakers
Their Christmas hymn.
——*Dorothy Neal White*

Goat Comes to the Christmas Party

"HURRY! HURRY! HURRY!" said Gran'ma to Araminta. "It's time to go to the party."

"Hurry! Hurry! Hurry!" said Araminta to Jerome Anthony. "It's time to go to the party."

Christmas had come to the country, and there was going to be a party at the schoolhouse. Everybody was going, so Araminta and Jerome Anthony and Gran'ma had to hurry, else they'd be late and miss something.

"I wish Goat could go to the party," said Araminta, shaking her head sadly. "It seems a shame that Goat can't have any Christmas at all."

"Goats don't have Christmas," laughed Jerome Anthony. "What ever would Goat do at a party?"

"Hurry! Hurry! Hurry!" said Gran'ma, looking at her watch.

So they put on their hats and coats and mittens. They tied their scarfs under their chins, and they started out. It was cold, so they walked fast and it didn't take any time to get to the schoolhouse. If they hadn't hurried they might have been late, for the party was just about to begin.

Everyone was there sitting on the school benches that were pushed back against the wall of the room. The beautiful paper chains and popcorn strings were there on the Christmas tree just where they belonged. And over in one corner was a table filled with cakes and lemonade and candy, for of course a party isn't a party without good things to eat.

"Where is Gran'pa?" asked Jerome Anthony, turning around in his seat. "I'm afraid Gran'pa is going to be late."

"Don't you worry," smiled Gran'ma. "Gran'pa will get here. He has a surprise for you."

"Surprise!" whispered Araminta, very excited. Then her face was sad. "Oh dear, I do wish Goat could be here for the surprise."

Just then there was a little noise at the back door and everyone turned around. Well, you can't imagine what they saw! Santa Claus! There he was in a red suit with white trimmings, and a red cap with a white tassel. And he had the reddest face you've ever seen, with a long white beard at the bottom of it.

"Oh! Oh!" yelled everybody.

"Shh-h-h!" whispered everybody.

For Santa Claus had somebody with him. This somebody was black and white with long floppy ears and a short stumpy tail. This somebody had long curly horns that looked very much like the branches of a tree. This somebody was hitched to a new green wagon. Yes, you've guessed it, Santa Claus had a reindeer with him, and this reindeer was pulling a wagon full of toys!

"Oh! Oh! Oh!" yelled everybody.

"Shh-h-h-h!" whispered everybody.

For Santa Claus and the reindeer were starting up the aisle toward the Christmas tree. They walked along steadily until they came to a bench where Jerome Anthony and Araminta were sitting, and then something very queer happened. That reindeer lifted his stumpy tail; he shook his head and his ears went flip-flop.

"GOAT!" yelled Araminta, jumping up and down. "Goat has come to the party!"

We can't be sure whether it was Araminta yelling or the sight of the Christmas tree, but anyway, just then that Santa Claus reindeer stopped acting like a reindeer and began acting like a goat instead. He butted Santa Claus out of the way. He broke loose from his wagon. He began *eating* the Christmas tree!

"Hey! Watch out!" said Santa Claus, falling against one of the benches. When he got up, that red face with the long white beard had fallen off.

"Gran'pa!" yelled Jerome Anthony. "Gran'pa got here after all!"

We can't be sure whether it was Jerome Anthony yelling or the sight of that goat eating the Christmas tree, but anyway, Santa Claus stopped acting like Santa Claus and began to act like Gran'pa instead. He grabbed hold of Goat. But every time he tried to stop Goat eating the popcorn off the tree, Goat reared up and butted him against the benches again.

"Let me help," said Araminta, jumping up. "I can manage that Goat."

She grabbed Goat by his bridle and started to lead him away before he ruined the tree. But just then Goat caught sight of the table full of cakes and candy and lemonade, and he pulled toward that.

Now when goats see something that they want to eat, you know how hard it is to keep them away from it. Araminta pulled and pulled, but it didn't do any good. Goat kept on getting closer and closer to that table of good food.

"Oh! Oh! Oh!" everybody yelled. They didn't want all their party refreshments to be eaten up.

"Shh-h-h!" everybody whispered, because it looked as if Jerome Anthony was going to do something about it.

He took two pieces of chocolate cake from the table and he held them out to Goat.

"Here, Goat!" he said.

Goat looked at that cake held out for him to eat; he reared up on his hind legs and shook those pretend-like reindeer horns off his short horns; then he ran after Jerome Anthony! Jerome Anthony ran down the middle of the schoolhouse, holding that cake so Goat could see it. Goat ran after him.

"Humph!" said Araminta, taking a deep breath, "I shouldn't have worried about Goat not having any Christmas. He had more than anybody else."

Gran'pa put on his red face with the white whiskers and there he was—a Santa Claus again. "Merry Christmas!" he laughed as he began to give out the toys. "Merry Christmas!" yelled everybody.

"Maa-aa! Maa-a-a!" came Goat's voice from the school-house yard.

But nobody opened the door to let him in.

———*Eva Knox Evans*

In the Week When Christmas Comes

This is the week when Christmas comes.

Let every pudding burst with plums,
And every tree bear dolls and drums,
   In the week when Christmas comes.

Let every hall have boughs of green,
With berries glowing in between,
   In the week when Christmas comes.

Let every doorstep have a song
Sounding the dark street along,
   In the week when Christmas comes.

Let every steeple ring a bell
With a joyful tale to tell,
   In the week when Christmas comes.

Let every night put forth a star
To show us where the heavens are,
   In the week when Christmas comes.

Let every stable have a lamb
Sleeping warm besides its dam,
   In the week when Christmas comes.

This is the week when Christmas comes.
      ——*Eleanor Farjeon*

A Merry Christmas

JO WAS THE FIRST to wake in the gray dawn of Christmas morning. No stockings hung at the fireplace, and for a moment she felt as much disappointed as she did long ago, when her little sock fell down because it was so crammed with goodies. Then she remembered her mother's promise, and slipping her hand under her pillow, drew out a little crimson-covered book. She knew it very well, for it was that beautiful old story of the best life ever lived, and Jo felt that it was a true guidebook for any pilgrim going the long journey. She woke Meg with a "Merry Christmas," and bade her see what was under her pillow. A green-covered book appeared, with the same picture inside, and a few words written by their mother, which made their one present very precious in

"A Merry Christmas" is from *Little Women*, by Louisa May Alcott. Reprinted by permission of Little Brown & Company.

their eyes. Presently Beth and Amy woke, to rummage and find their little books also—one dove-colored, the other blue; and all sat looking at and talking about them, while the east grew rosy with the coming day.

In spite of her small vanities, Margaret had a sweet and pious nature, which unconsciously influenced her sisters, especially Jo, who loved her very tenderly, and obeyed her because her advice was so gently given.

"Girls," said Meg seriously, looking from the tumbled head beside her to the two little nightcapped ones in the room beyond, "mother wants us to read and love and mind these books, and we must begin at once. We used to be faithful about it; but since father went away, and all this war trouble unsettled us, we have neglected many things. You can do as you please; but I shall keep my book on the table here, and read a little every morning as soon as I wake, for I know it will do me good, and help me through the day."

Then she opened her new book and began to read. Jo put her arm around her, and, leaning cheek to cheek, read also, with the quiet expression so seldom seen on her restless face.

"How good Meg is! Come, Amy, let's do as they do. I'll help you with the hard words, and they'll explain things if we don't understand," whispered Beth, very much impressed by the pretty books and her sisters' example.

"I'm glad mine is blue," said Amy; and then the rooms were very still while the pages were softly turned, and the winter sunshine crept in to touch the bright heads and serious faces with a Christmas greeting.

"Where is mother?" asked Meg, as she and Jo ran

down to thank her for their gifts, half an hour later.

"Goodness only knows. Some poor creeter comes a-beggin', and your ma went straight off to see what was needed. There never was such a woman for givin' away vittles and drink, clothes and firin'," replied Hannah, who had lived with the family since Meg was born, and was considered by them all more as a friend than a servant.

"She will be back soon, I think: so fry your cakes, and have everything ready," said Meg, looking over the presents which were collected in a basket and kept under the sofa, ready to be produced at the proper time. "Why, where is Amy's bottle of cologne?" she added, as the little flask did not appear.

"She took it out a minute ago, and went off with it to put a ribbon on it, or some such notion," replied Jo, dancing about the room to take the first stiffness off the new army slippers.

"How nice my handkerchiefs look, don't they? Hannah washed and ironed them for me, and I marked them all myself," said Beth, looking proudly at the somewhat uneven letters which had cost her such labor.

"Bless the child! She's gone and put 'Mother' on them instead of 'M. March.' How funny!" cried Jo, taking up one.

"Isn't it right? I thought it was better to do it so, because Meg's initials are 'M. M.', and I don't want anyone to use these but Marmee," said Beth, looking troubled.

"It's all right, dear, and a very pretty idea—quite sensible, too, for no one can ever mistake now. It will please her very much, I know," said Meg, with a frown for Jo and a smile for Beth.

"There's mother. Hide the basket, quick!" cried Jo, as a door slammed, and steps sounded in the hall.

Amy came in hastily, and looked rather abashed when she saw her sisters all waiting for her.

"Where have you been, and what are you hiding behind you?" asked Meg, surprised to see, by her hood and cloak, that lazy Amy had been out so early.

"Don't laugh at me, Jo! I didn't mean anyone should know till the time came. I only meant to change the little bottle for a big one, and I gave all my money to get it, and I'm truly trying not to be selfish any more."

As she spoke, Amy showed the handsome flask which replaced the cheap one; and looked so earnest and humble in her little effort to forget herself that Meg hugged her on the spot, and Jo pronounced her "a trump," while Beth ran to the window, and picked her finest rose to ornament the stately bottle.

"You see I felt ashamed of my present, after reading and talking about being good this morning, so I ran round the corner and changed it the minute I was up; and I'm so glad, for mine is the handsomest now."

Another bang of the street door sent the basket under the sofa, and the girls to the table, eager for breakfast.

"Merry Christmas, Marmee! Many of them! Thank you for our books; we read some, and mean to every day," they cried, in chorus.

"Merry Christmas, little daughters! I'm glad you began at once, and hope you will keep on. But I want to say one word before we sit down. Not far away from here lies a poor woman with a newborn baby. Six children are huddled into one bed to keep from freezing, for they have no fire. There is nothing to eat over there; and the oldest boy came to tell me they were suffering hunger and cold. My girls, will you give them your breakfast as a Christmas present?"

They were all unusually hungry, having waited nearly an hour, and for a minute no one spoke; only a minute, for Jo exclaimed impetuously:

"I'm so glad you came before we began!"

"May I go and help carry the things to the poor little children?" asked Beth eagerly.

"I shall take the cream and muffins," added Amy, heroically giving up the articles she most liked.

Meg was already covering the buckwheats, and piling the bread into one big plate.

"I thought you'd do it," said Mrs. March, smiling as if satisfied. "You shall all go and help me, and when we come back we will have bread and milk for breakfast, and make it up at dinnertime."

They were soon ready, and the procession set out. Fortunately it was early, and they went through back streets, so few people saw them, and no one laughed at the queer party.

A poor, bare, miserable room it was, with broken windows, no fire, ragged bedclothes, a sick mother, wailing baby, and a group of pale, hungry children cuddled under one old quilt, trying to keep warm.

How the big eyes stared and the blue lips smiled as the girls went in!

"Ach, mein Gott! It is good angels come to us!" said the poor woman, crying for joy.

"Funny angels in hoods and mittens," said Jo, and set them laughing.

In a few minutes it really did seem as if kind spirits

had been at work there. Hannah, who had carried wood, made a fire, and stopped up the broken panes with old hats and her own cloak. Mrs. March gave the mother tea and gruel, and comforted her with promises of help, while she dressed the little baby as tenderly as if it had been her own. The girls, meantime, spread the table, set the children round the fire, and fed them like so many hungry birds—laughing, talking, and trying to understand the funny broken English.

"Das ist gut!" "Die Engel-kinder!" cried the poor things, as they ate, and warmed their purple hands at the comfortable blaze.

The girls had never been called angel children before, and thought it very agreeable, especially Jo, who had been considered a "Sancho" ever since she was born. That was a very happy breakfast, though they didn't get any of it, and when they went away, leaving comfort behind, I think there were not in all the city four merrier people than the hungry little girls who gave away their breakfasts and contented themselves with bread and milk on Christmas morning.

"That's loving our neighbor better than ourselves, and I like it," said Meg, as they set out their presents, while their mother was upstairs collecting clothes for the poor Hummels.

Not a very splendid show, but there was a great deal of love done up in the few little bundles; and the tall vase of red roses, white chrysanthemums, and trailing vines, which stood in the middle, gave quite an elegant air to the table.

"She's coming! Strike up, Beth! Open the door, Amy! Three cheers for Marmee!" cried Jo, prancing about.

while Meg went to conduct mother to the seat of honor.

Beth played her gayest march, Amy threw open the door, and Meg enacted escort with great dignity. Mrs. March was both surprised and touched; and smiled with her eyes full as she examined her presents, and read the little notes which accompanied them. The slippers went on at once, a new handkerchief was slipped into her pocket, well scented with Amy's cologne, the rose was fastened in her bosom, and the nice gloves were pronounced a "perfect fit."

There was a good deal of laughing and kissing and explaining, in the simple, loving fashion which makes these home festivals so pleasant at the time, so sweet to remember long afterward, and then all fell to work.

The morning charities and ceremonies took so much time that the rest of the day was devoted to preparations for the evening festivities. Being still too young to go often to the theater, and not rich enough to afford any great outlay for private performances, the girls put their wits to work, and—necessity being the mother of invention—made whatever they needed. Very clever were some of their productions—pasteboard guitars, antique lamps made of old-fashioned butter boats covered with silver paper, gorgeous robes of old cotton, glittering with tin spangles from a pickle factory, and armor covered with the same useful diamond-shaped bits, left in sheets when the lids of tin preserve pots were cut out. The furniture was used to being turned topsy-turvy, and the big chamber was the scene of many innocent revels.

No gentlemen were admitted; so Jo played male parts to her heart's content, and took immense satisfaction in a pair of russet-leather boots given her by a friend, who knew a lady who knew an actor. These boots, an old foil, and a slashed doublet once used by an artist for some picture, were Jo's chief treasures, and appeared on all occasions. The smallness of the company made it necessary for the two principal actors to take several parts apiece; and they certainly deserved some credit for the hard work they did in learning three or four different parts, whisking in and out of various costumes, and managing the stage besides. It was excellent drill for their memories, a harmless amusement, and employed many hours which otherwise would have been idle, lonely, or spent in less profitable society.

On Christmas night, a dozen girls piled onto the bed which was the dress circle, and sat before the blue and yellow chintz curtains in a most flattering state of expectancy. There was a good deal of rustling and whispering behind the curtain, a trifle of lamp smoke, and an occasional giggle from Amy, who was apt to get hysterical in the excitement of the moment. Presently a bell sounded, the curtains flew apart, and the Operatic Tragedy began.

"A gloomy wood," according to the one playbill, was represented by a few shrubs in pots, green baize on the floor, and a cave in the distance. This cave was made with a clotheshorse for a roof, bureaus for walls; and in it was a small furnace in full blast, with a black pot on it, and an old witch bending over it. The stage was dark, and the glow of the furnace had a fine effect, especially as real steam issued from the kettle when the witch took off the cover. A moment was allowed for the first thrill to subside; then Hugo, the villain, stalked in with a clanking sword at his side, a slouched hat, black beard, mysterious cloak, and the boots. After pacing to and fro in much agitation, he struck his forehead, and burst out in a wild strain, singing of his hatred to Roderigo, his love for Zara, and his pleasing resolution to kill the one and win the other. The gruff tones of Hugo's voice, with an occasional shout when his feelings overcame him, were very impressive, and the audience applauded the moment he paused for breath. Bowing with the air of one accustomed to public praise, he stole to the cavern, and ordered Hagar to come forth with a commanding "What ho, minion! I need thee!"

Out came Meg, with gray horsehair hanging about her face, a red and black robe, a staff, and cabalistic signs upon her cloak. Hugo demanded a potion to make Zara adore him, and one to destroy Roderigo. Hagar, in a fine dramatic melody, promised both, and proceeded to call up the spirit who would bring the love philter:

> "Hither, hither, from thy home,
> Airy spirit, I bid thee come!
> Born of roses, fed on dew,
> Charms and potions canst thou brew?
> Bring me here, with elfin speed,
> The fragrant philter which I need;
> Make it sweet and swift and strong,
> Spirit, answer now my song!"

A soft strain of music sounded, and then at the back of the cave appeared a little figure in cloudy white, with glittering wings, golden hair, and a garland of roses on its head. Waving a wand, it sang:

> "Hither I come,
> From my airy home,

Afar in the silver moon.
Take the magic spell,
And use it well,
Or its power will vanish soon!"

And, dropping a small, gilded bottle at the witch's feet, the spirit vanished. Another chant from Hagar produced another apparition—not a lovely one; for, with a bang, an ugly black imp appeared, and having croaked a reply, tossed a dark bottle at Hugo, and disappeared with a mocking laugh. Having warbled his thanks and put the potions in his boots, Hugo departed; and Hagar informed the audience that, as he had killed a few of her friends in times past, she has cursed him, and intends to thwart his plans, and be revenged on him. Then the curtain fell, and the audience reposed and ate candy while discussing the merits of the play.

A good deal of hammering went on before the curtain rose again; but when it became evident what a masterpiece of stage carpentering had been got up, no one murmured at the delay. It was truly superb! A tower rose to the ceiling; halfway up appeared a window, with a lamp burning at it, and behind the white curtain appeared Zara in a lovely blue and silver dress, waiting for Roderigo. He came in gorgeous array, with plumed cap, red cloak, chestnut lovelocks, a guitar, and the boots, of course. Kneeling at the foot of the tower, he sang a serenade in melting tones. Zara replied, and, after a musical dialogue, consented to fly. Then came the grand effect of the play. Roderigo produced a rope ladder, with five steps to it, threw up one end, and invited Zara to descend. Timidly she crept from her lattice, put her hand on Roderigo's shoulder, and was about to leap gracefully down, when "Alas! Alas for Zara!" she forgot her train—it caught in the window; the tower tottered, leaned forward, fell with a crash, and buried the unhappy lovers in the ruins!

A universal shriek arose as the russet boots waved wildly from the wreck, and a golden head emerged, exclaiming, "I told you so!" With wonderful presence of mind, Don Pedro, the cruel sire, rushed in, dragged out his daughter, with a hasty aside:

"Don't laugh! Act as if it was all right!"—and, ordering Roderigo up, banished him from the kingdom with wrath and scorn. Though decidedly shaken by the fall of the tower upon him, Roderigo defied the old gentleman, and refused to stir. This dauntless example fired Zara: she also defied her sire, and he ordered them both to the deepest dungeons of the castle. A stout little retainer came in with chains, and led them away, looking very much frightened, and evidently forgetting the speech he ought to have made.

Act third was the castle hall; and here Hagar appeared, having come to free the lovers and finish Hugo. She hears him coming, and hides; sees him put the potions into two cups of wine, and bid the timid little servant "Bear them to the captives in their cells, and tell them I shall come anon." The servant takes Hugo aside to tell him something, and Hagar changes the cups for two others which are harmless. Ferdinando, the "minion," carries them away, and Hagar puts back the cup which holds the poison meant for Roderigo. Hugo, getting thirsty after a long warble, drinks it, loses his wits, and, after a good deal of clutching and stamping, falls flat and dies; while

Hagar informs him what she has done in a song of exquisite power and melody.

This was a truly thrilling scene, though some persons might have thought that the sudden tumbling down of a quantity of long hair rather marred the effect of the villain's death. He was called before the curtain, and with great propriety appeared, leading Hagar, whose singing was considered more wonderful than all the rest of the performance put together.

Act fourth displayed the despairing Roderigo on the point of stabbing himself, because he has been told that Zara has deserted him. Just as the dagger is at his heart, a lovely song is sung under his window, informing him that Zara is true, but in danger, and he can save her, if he will. A key is thrown in, which unlocks the door, and in a spasm of rapture he tears off his chains, and rushes away to find and rescue his ladylove.

Act fifth opened with a stormy scene between Zara and Don Pedro. He wishes her to go into a convent, but she won't hear of it; and, after a touching appeal, is about to faint, when Roderigo dashes in and demands her hand. Don Pedro refuses, because he is not rich. They shout and gesticulate tremendously, but cannot agree, and Roderigo is about to bear away the exhausted Zara when the timid servant enters with a letter and a bag from Hagar, who has mysteriously disappeared. The letter informs the party that she bequeaths untold wealth to the young pair, and an awful doom to Don Pedro, if he doesn't make them happy. The bag is opened, and several quarts of tin money shower down upon the stage, till it is quite glorified with the glitter. This entirely softens the "stern sire": he consents with a murmur, all join in a joyful chorus, and the curtain falls upon the lovers kneeling to receive Don Pedro's blessing in attitudes of the most romantic grace.

Tumultuous applause followed, but received an unexpected check; for the cot bed, on which the "dress circle" was built, suddenly shut up, and extinguished the enthusiastic audience. Roderigo and Don Pedro flew to the rescue, and all were taken out unhurt, though many were speechless with laughter. The excitement had hardly subsided when Hannah appeared, with "Mrs. March's compliments, and would the ladies walk down to supper."

This was a surprise, even to the actors; and, when they saw the table, they looked at one another in rapturous amazement. It was like Marmee to get up a little treat for them; but anything so fine as this was unheard of since the departed days of plenty. There was ice cream—actually two dishes of it, pink and white—and cake and fruit and distracting French bonbons, and, in the middle of the table, four great bouquets of hothouse flowers!

It quite took their breath away; and they stared first at the table and then at their mother, who looked as if she enjoyed it immensely.

"Is it fairies?" asked Amy.

"It's Santa Claus," said Beth.

"Mother did it"; and Meg smiled her sweetest, in spite of her gray beard and white eyebrows.

"Aunt March had a good fit, and sent the supper," cried Jo, with a sudden inspiration.

"All wrong. Old Mr. Laurence sent it," replied Mrs. March.

"The Laurence boy's grandfather! What in the world

put such a thing into his head? We don't know him!"
exclaimed Meg.

"Hannah told one of his servants about your breakfast
party. He is an odd old gentleman, but that pleased him.
He knew my father, years ago; and he sent me a polite
note this afternoon, saying he hoped I would allow him
to express his friendly feeling toward my children by
sending them a few trifles in honor of the day. I could
not refuse; and so you have a little feast at night to make
up for the bread-and-milk breakfast."

"That boy put it into his head, I know he did! He's a
capital fellow, and I wish we could get acquainted. He
looks as if he'd like to know us; but he's bashful, and
Meg is so prim she won't let me speak to him when we
pass," said Jo, as the plates went around, and the ice began
to melt out of sight, with "Ohs!" and "Ahs!" of satisfaction.

"You mean the people who live in the big house next
door, don't you?" asked one of the girls. "My mother
knows old Mr. Laurence but says he's very proud, and
doesn't like to mix with his neighbors. He keeps his grandson shut up, when he isn't riding or walking with his
tutor, and makes him study very hard. We invited him
to our party, but he didn't come. Mother says he's very
nice, though he never speaks to us girls."

"Our cat ran away once, and he brought her back, and
we talked over the fence, and were getting on capitally—
all about cricket, and so on—when he saw Meg coming,
and walked off. I mean to know him someday; for he
needs fun, I'm sure he does," said Jo decidedly.

"I like his manners, and he looks like a little gentleman;
so I've no objection to your knowing him, if a proper

opportunity comes. He brought the flowers himself; and I should have asked him in, if I had been sure what was going on upstairs. He looked so wistful as he went away, hearing the frolic, and evidently having none of his own."

"It's a mercy you didn't, mother!" laughed Jo, looking at her boots. "But we'll have another play, sometime, that he can see. Perhaps he'll help act; wouldn't that be jolly?"

"I never had such a fine bouquet before! How pretty it is!" And Meg examined her flowers with great interest.

"They are lovely! But Beth's roses are sweeter to me," said Mrs. March, smelling the half-dead posy in her belt.

Beth nestled up to her, and whispered softly, "I wish I could send my bunch to father. I'm afraid he isn't having such a merry Christmas as we are."

———*Louisa May Alcott*

A Christmas Carol

God bless the master of this house,
   The mistress also,
And all the little children
   That round the table go.

And all your kin and kinsmen
   That dwell both far and near,
I wish you a merry Christmas
   And a happy New Year!
         ——*Old English Carol*

Christmas in the Gaspé

ALL THE MORNING, on the day before Christmas, the house was filled with excitement and bustle. The kitchen was full of many good smells, for Tante Eugenie was baking all kinds of things. For the past two weeks she had been baking cookies and cakes, and several crocks stood full on the shelf.

The rabbits were dressed and cleaned ready for the reveillon ragout. The pea soup was bubbling on the back of the stove all ready for supper. The lovely tree stood in its corner of the parlor with the angel at the top, and candles on the tips of the branches ready to be lighted. All the house was shining clean.

Suzanne, Tante Eugenie and Berthe were dressed in their best waiting for Uncle Jacques and Andre to be ready. Cippy and Paule were scrubbed and dressed, Cippy's hair in little damp curls and Paule's tied back with a ribbon. It seemed like Sunday, but of course it wasn't! It was almost Christmas Eve! Pretty soon, Uncle Jacques called in the door and they all went to the church for confession before Midnight Mass.

When they came back, each one brought to Tante Eugenie their gifts for the tree from their hiding places. Such mystery! Such tiptoeing! Suzanne saw Uncle Jacques come out of the door to the parlor, and close it quickly behind him. She heard a rustle of paper and saw Tante Eugenie slip something behind her as she closed the door to the little cupboard under the stairs. Andre kept something under his coat until he got past the kitchen, then he gave it to Tante, who opened the door just a crack. They whispered for a moment, then the door was shut again. It was hard to keep Cippy and Paule from seeing. They were all eyes and ears, and so excited they couldn't keep still. Every time the parlor door opened they craned their necks to see.

"Va t'en! Va t'en!"—Go away! Tante Eugenie scolded. Then they would be good for a few minutes, and turn somersaults all over the kitchen. They nearly squashed Pouf, so he took refuge under the stove.

Suzanne brought downstairs the gifts she had, and whispered to Uncle Jacques to put them on the tree for her. She didn't want Tante Eugenie to even see the package that smelled like perfume. She had wrapped the scarf in a piece of red tissue that Mr. Ryan had given her, and had written a name carefully on each package. Pepere sat quietly by the stove smoking his pipe. He didn't seem very much excited, but he looked happy.

Tante Eugenie kept going back and forth, into the kitchen, up the stairs, into the little cupboard, even down to the cellar. What could be down there! Cippy and Paule got down on their hands and knees to look when the trap door was open but they couldn't see, and when Tante came up she kept whatever it was under her apron.

It seemed to Suzanne that the time would never come for the tree and reveillon. She got out her pencil and tablet, and began to draw a picture of the tree. She wished again she had some paints like the tourist lady had. The colors would be so lovely on her picture.

It was dark before Tante Eugenie and Uncle Jacques had everything ready. Since the day before Christmas is a fast day, there was only pea soup for supper. The little ones must say their prayers and go to bed to rest until time for the Midnight Mass. Suzanne thought she never could go to sleep, but she was soon deep in dreams.

She was wakened by Berthe, who took her hand and whispered so as not to wake Cippy and Paule. They were too small to go and Pepere was too old, so he stayed at home with them.

They must all wrap up well; it was cold. Suzanne wished she hadn't lost her mittens, but the old one of Berthe's was better than none, and she would walk beside Uncle Jacques and put her hand in his.

As they turned out of the lane, people were coming from further down the road, crunching along in the snow, the frosty air making their voices sound close.

"Joyeux Noel!" Merry Christmas! they called as they passed. "Noel, Noel!" The church bells began to ring.

Suzanne shivered with excitement and looked up at the stars that filled the sky. One star looked especially bright. It looked as if it stood right over the church, and Suzanne thought it might be the Star of Bethlehem!

"So," said Uncle Jacques, as he squeezed her hand, "it is Noel! You are 'appy, eh, Ti-Su?" He swept her along beside him, her feet scarcely touching the ground.

"Oh, oui!" Suzanne laughed back at him, and skipped as much as she could skip with the heavy boots on her feet.

All along the way to the church, dark figures joined them from each lane and gateway. From each one came the greeting, "Joyeux Noel! Joyeux Noel!"

The church looked beautiful. The pillars were wrapped with greens, there were branches of evergreen on the window sills, and a tall pine tree stood at each side of the altar. Soft candlelight showed the gilt edge on the Virgin's blue robe, reflected in the gold altar service, lighted the figure of a saint, and made real the little carved figures of the creche at the left of the altar. The shepherds were kneeling in real straw, the Ste. Vierge was sitting on a real little wooden bench, and the tiny Christ Child was lying in a real little manger made of wood. Suzanne could see it all very plainly from where she was sitting. Softly, the choir began to sing, "Adeste Fidelis." Then the altar boys, two by two, with lighted candles, came slowly down the aisle. The tiny ones first, Etienne and little Jean, then Paule and Leonard and the others, the older ones next, and then the big boys like Andre and Jules. They looked very solemn, and hardly like the same boys that played so roughly every day.

After the service, Tante Eugenie invited Ol 'Batees' to

come home with them to the reveillon. He was glad to come and said he would bring his fiddle.

Such laughing and talking! Such a shouting of "Happy Christmas!" Everyone was in a good humor, everyone seemed very happy.

It didn't take long for Tante Eugenie to get the supper on the table. Uncle Jacques got out the jug of home-made wine and Ol 'Batees' got out his fiddle.

Suzanne and Andre and Berthe danced around the kitchen. "Ol 'Batees', he dance too," he said, his thick boots clumping on the floor.

The fire in the stove was snapping and cracking, the teakettle was humming, the fiddle was singing under Ol 'Batees' fingers, the children were laughing and dancing.

Then Tante Eugenie called them all to the table. All was quiet for a moment while they blessed themselves, then all broke into happy cries of "Joyeux Noel!" as they sat down to the feast.

Then came the time for the gifts. Suzanne's throat ached with excitement. Cippy and Paule were standing at the door of the parlor, waiting for Uncle Jacques to carry in the lamp and to light the candles on the tree. At last he threw open the door. There stood the beautiful tree with little packages tied all over it, and at the base! Oh, Suzanne just couldn't believe her eyes! She sat down on the floor with the other children, in front of Pepere and Tante Eugenie. Uncle Jacques was to hand out the gifts.

"Aha!" he said, "here is somet'ing for good little girls." To Cippy he gave a cradle and to Paule a small cart. There were warm socks for Uncle Jacques, for Pepere, and for Andre, that Tante Eugenie had knitted, a dress for Berthe that Tante Eugenie had made from one of her own. Then Uncle Jacques picked up and hid behind him what Suzanne had seen peeking out from under the tree. She saw Uncle Jacques' eyes twinkle as he looked at her.

"So," he said, "now de pe ti' Suzanne can go, vite! vite! over de snow." And he gave her the most beautiful pair of snowshoes she had ever seen. She was so happy she hugged them to her and didn't say a word, but put them down long enough to throw her arms around Uncle Jacques as far as they would go. Next, came a pair of skis for Andre. "So, that is why there were always wood splinters on the floor in the mornings!" Andre was as delighted as Ti-Su.

Suzanne held her breath while Andre unwrapped the scarf. She wanted to see what Tante Eugenie would say, too, when she saw it.

"I made it all myself!" she said as Andre's eyes opened in surprise. "Tch! Tch!" said Tante, "you mak' de weave?" She held up the scarf and shook her head. "Eet is beautiful!"

Then Ol 'Batees' said, " 'Ere ees somet'ing soft for de little Zuzanne," and threw it into her lap. She undid the wrapping with fingers that trembled. Oh, that good Tante Eugenie! She had knitted a new pair of red mittens for Suzanne. That was what she had been hiding in the little cupboard under the stairs for such a long time.

Then Uncle Jacques reached up and took off the tree the little package Suzanne had bought for Tante Eugenie.

"Umm," he said, "it smell good. Gif' for a lady!" And gave it to Tante Eugenie. Suzanne could hardly wait till she took off the red string and undid the paper. Maybe she wouldn't like it. But how could she help it? It was so sweet. Tante Eugenie took off the last scrap of paper and what do you think it was? A little Cupid made of soap! Tante Eugenie did like it, even if her eyes were filled with tears. Grownups don't usually get presents. Then Uncle Jacques handed to Suzanne the package from the United States. Everyone watched to see what was in that package! Suzanne opened it. A card dropped out: "For Ti-Su who would love to paint!" And there was a box of beautiful water colors and brushes from the tourist lady!

The candles were burning low and all the gifts had been taken from the tree. It was almost morning, and Cippy was yawning. Paule was asleep against Berthe's shoulder, Pepere was nodding in his chair, and Tante Eugenie could hardly keep her eyes open.

Ol 'Batees' said, "Merci! madame, for de good reveillon," and once again he said, "Joyeux Noel!" and left.

What a happy time it had been. Andre went up to the loft, and all the children went up the stairs to bed, with Berthe to help them. Suzanne didn't even notice the long shadows up the wall; she knew that the strange bundle on the chair was only Tante Eugenie's old dress, that the moaning sound she heard was only the wind in the sycamore tree.

She heard the sleepy murmuring of Cippy and Paule as they said their prayers for Berthe. She said her own and crept into bed. She sighed with happiness at the thought of the snowshoes and the mittens and the beautiful paints; of how Andre had loved the scarf she had made him; of how Tante Eugenie loved the sweet little soap baby; and of how Uncle Jacques would enjoy the tobacco.

She opened her eyes once more, and there, shining in her window, was the bright star. It shone softly and seemed to say, "Joyeux Noel, Joyeux Noel."

——*Marguerite de Angeli*

Christmas Song

Why do bells for Christmas ring?
Why do little children sing?

Once a lovely shining star,
Seen by shepherds from afar,
Gently moved until its light
Made a manger's cradle bright.

There a darling baby lay,
Pillowed soft upon the hay;
And its mother sang and smiled,
"This is Christ, the holy Child!"

Therefore bells for Christmas ring,
Therefore little children sing.
                    ——Eugene Field

The Voyage of the Wee Red Cap

IT WAS THE EVE of St. Stephen, and Teig sat alone by his fire with naught in his cupboard but a pinch of tea and a bare mixing of meal, and a heart inside of him as soft and warm as the ice on the water-bucket outside the door. The turf was near burnt on the hearth—a handful of golden cinders left, just; and Teig took to counting them greedily on his fingers.

"There's one, two, three, an' four an' five," he laughed. "Faith, there be more bits o' real gold hid undther the loose clay in the corner."

It was the truth; and it was the scraping and scrooching for the last piece that had left Teig's cupboard bare of a Christmas dinner.

"Gold is bether nor eatin' an' dthrinkin'. An' if ye have naught to give, there'll be naught asked of ye." And he laughed again.

He was thinking of the neighbors, and the doles of food and piggins of milk that would pass over their thresholds that night to the vagabonds and paupers who were sure to come begging. And on the heels of that thought followed another: who would be giving old Shawn his dinner? Shawn lived a stone's throw from Teig, alone, in a wee tumbled-in cabin; and for a score of years past Teig had stood on the door-step every Christmas Eve, and, making a hollow of his two hands, had called across the road:

"Hey, there, Shawn, will ye come over for a sup?"

And Shawn had reached for his crutches, there being but one leg to him, and had come.

"Faith," said Teig, trying another laugh. "Shawn can fast for the once; 'twill be all the same in a month's time." And he fell to thinking of the gold again.

A knock came to the door. Teig pulled himself down in his chair where the shadow would cover him, and held his tongue.

"Teig, Teig!" It was the Widow O'Donnelly's voice. "If ye are there, open your door. I have not got the pay for the spriggin' this month, an' the childther are needin' food."

But Teig put the leash on his tongue, and never stirred till he heard the tramp of her feet going on to the next cabin. Then he saw to it that the door was tight barred. Another knock came, and it was a stranger's voice this time.

"The other cabins are filled; not one but has its hearth

crowded. Will ye take us in, the two of us? The wind bites mortal sharp; not a morsel o' food have we tasted this day. Masther, will ye take us in?"

But Teig sat on, a-holding his tongue; and the tramp of the stranger's feet passed down the road. Others took their place—small feet, running. It was the miller's wee Cassie, and she called out as she went by:

"Old Shawn's watchin' for ye. Ye'll not be forgettin' him, will ye, Teig?"

And then the child broke into a song, sweet and clear, as she passed down the road:

"Listen all ye, 'tis the Feast o' St. Stephen,
Mind that ye keep it, this holy even.
Open your door and greet ye the stranger,
For ye mind that the wee Lord had naught but a manger.
                                        Mhuire as truagh!
"Feed ye the hungry and rest ye the weary.
This ye must do for the sake of Our Mary.
'Tis well that ye mind—ye who sit by the fire—
That the Lord He was born in a dark and cold byre.
                                        Mhuire as truagh!"

Teig put his fingers deep in his ears. "A million murdthering curses on them that won't let me be! Can't a man try to keep what is his without bein' pesthered by them that has only idled and wasted their days?"

And then the strange thing happened: hundreds and hundreds of wee lights began dancing outside the window, making the room bright; the hands of the clock began chasing each other round the dial, and the bolt of the door drew itself out. Slowly, without a creak or a cringe, the door opened, and in there trooped a crowd of the

Good People. Their wee green cloaks were folded close about them, and each carried a rush-candle.

Teig was filled with a great wonderment, entirely, when he saw the fairies, but when they saw him they laughed.

"We are takin' the loan o' your cabin this night, Teig," said they. "Ye are the only man hereabouts with an empty hearth, an' we're needin' one."

Without saying more, they bustled about the room making ready. They lengthened out the table and spread and set it; more of the Good People trooped in, bringing stools and food and drink. The pipers came last, and they sat themselves around the chimney-piece a-blowing their chanters and trying the drones. The feasting began and the pipers played, and never had Teig seen such a sight in his life. Suddenly a wee man sang out:

"Clip, clap, clip, clap, I wish I had my wee red cap!"

And out of the air there tumbled the neatest cap Teig had ever laid his two eyes on. The wee man clapped it on his head, crying:

"I wish I was in Spain!" And—whist!—up the chimney he went, and away out of sight!

It happened just as I am telling it. Another wee man called for his cap, and away he went after the first. And then another and another until the room was empty and Teig sat alone again.

"By my soul," said Teig, "I'd like to thravel like that myself! It's a grand savin' of tickets an' baggage; an ye' get to a place before ye've had time to change your mind. Faith, there is no harm done if I thry it."

So he sang the fairies' rhyme and out of the air dropped a wee cap for him. For a moment the wonder had him, but the next he was clapping the cap on his head, crying: "Spain!"

Then—whist!—up the chimney he went after the fairies, and before he had time to let out his breath he was standing in the middle of Spain, and strangeness all about him.

He was in a great city. The doorways of the houses were hung with flowers and the air was warm and sweet with the smell of them. Torches burned along the streets, sweet-meat sellers went about crying their wares, and on the steps of a cathedral crouched a crowd of beggars.

"What's the meanin' o' that?" asked Teig of one of the fairies.

"They are waiting for those that are hearing Mass. When they come out they give half of what they have to those that have nothing, so that on this night of all the year there shall be no hunger and no cold."

And then far down the street came the sound of a child's voice, singing:

"Listen all ye, 'tis the Feast o' St. Stephen,
Mind that ye keep it, this holy even."

"Curse it!" said Teig. "Can a song fly afther ye?" And then he heard the fairies cry, "Holland!" and he cried, "Holland!" too.

In one leap he was over France, and another over Belgium, and with the third he was standing by long ditches of water frozen fast, and over them glided hundreds upon hundreds of lads and maids. Outside each door stood a wee wooden shoe, empty. Teig saw scores of them as he looked down the ditch of a street.

"What is the meanin' o' those shoes?" he asked the fairies.

"Ye poor lad!" answered the wee man next to him. "Are ye not knowing anything? This is the Gift Night of the year, when every man gives to his neighbor."

A child came to the window of one of the houses, and in her hand was a lighted candle. She was singing as she put the light down close to the glass, and Teig caught the words:

"Open your door and greet ye the stranger,

For ye mind that the wee Lord had naught but a manger.

Mhuire as truagh!"

" 'Tis the de'il's work!" cried Teig, and he set the red cap more firmly on his head. "I'm for another country."

I cannot be telling you half of the adventures Teig had that night, nor half the sights that he saw. But he passed by fields that held sheaves of grain for the birds, and door-steps that held bowls of porridge for the wee creatures. He saw lighted trees, sparkling and heavy with gifts; and he stood outside the churches and watched the crowds pass in, bearing gifts to the Holy Mother and Child.

At last the fairies straightened their caps and cried, "Now for the great hall in the King of England's palace!"

Whist!—and away they went, and Teig after them; and the first thing he knew he was in London, not an arm's-length from the King's throne. It was a grander sight than he had seen in any other country. The hall was filled entirely with lords and ladies; and the great doors were open for the poor and the homeless to come in and warm themselves by the King's fire and feast from the King's table. And many a hungry soul did the King serve with his own hands.

Those that had anything to give gave it in return. It

might be a bit of music played on a harp or a pipe, or it might be a dance or a song; but more often it was a wish, just, for good luck and safe-keeping.

Teig was so taken up with the watching that he never heard the fairies when they wished themselves off; moreover, he never saw the wee girl that was fed and went laughing away. But he heard a bit of her song as she passed through the door:

"Feed ye the hungry and rest ye the weary,
    This ye must do for the sake of our Mary."

Then the anger had Teig. "I'll stop your pestherin' tongue once an' for all time!" And, catching the cap from his head, he threw it after her.

No sooner was the cap gone than every soul in the hall saw him. The next moment they were about him, catching at his coat and crying:

"Where is he from? What does he here? Bring him before the King!"

And Teig was dragged along by a hundred hands to the throne where the King sat.

"He was stealing food," cried one.

"He was stealing the King's jewels," cried another.

"He looks evil," cried a third. "Kill him!"

And in a moment all the voices took it up and the hall rang with, "Aye, kill him, kill him!"

Teig's legs took to trembling, and fear put the leash on his tongue; but after a long silence he managed to whisper:

"I have done evil to no one, no one!"

"Maybe," said the King. "But have ye done good? Come, tell us, have ye given aught to any one this night? If ye have, we will pardon ye."

Not a word could Teig say; fear tightened the leash, for he was knowing full well there was no good to him that night.

"Then ye must die," said the King. "Will ye try hanging or beheading?"

"Hanging, please, your Majesty," said Teig.

The guards came rushing up and carried him off. But as he was crossing the threshold of the hall a thought sprang at him and held him.

"Your Majesty," he called after him, "will ye grant me a last request?"

"I will," said the King.

"Thank ye. There's a wee red cap that I'm mortal fond of, and I lost it awhile ago; if I could be hung with it on I would hang a deal more comfortable."

The cap was found and brought to Teig.

"Clip, clap, clip, clap, for my wee red cap. I wish I was home!" he sang.

Up and over the heads of the dumfounded guard he flew, and—whist!—and away out of sight. When he opened his eyes again he was sitting close by his own hearth, with the fire burnt low. The hands of the clock were still, the bolt was fixed firm in the door. The fairies' lights were gone, and the only bright thing was the candle burning in old Shawn's cabin across the road.

A running of feet sounded outside, and then the snatch of a song:

" 'Tis well that ye mind, ye who sit by the fire,
That the Lord He was born in a dark and cold byre.

Mhuire as truagh!"

"Wait ye, whoever ye are!" And Teig was away to the corner, digging fast at the loose clay, as the terrier digs at a bone. He filled his hands full of the shining gold, then hurried to the door, unbarring it.

The miller's wee Cassie stood there, peering at him out of the darkness.

"Take those to the Widow O'Donnelly, do ye hear? And take the rest to the store. Ye tell Jamie to bring up all that he has that is eatable an' dhrinkable; an' to the neighbors ye say, 'Teig's keepin' the feast this night.' Hurry now!"

Teig stopped a moment on the threshold until the tramp of her feet had died away; then he made a hollow of his hands and called across the road:

"Hey, there, Shawn, will ye come over for a sup?"

"And hey, there, the two o' ye, will ye come out for a sup?"

It was Johanna's cheery voice bringing David back from a strange country and stranger happenings. She stood in the open doorway, a lighted candle in her hand.

"Ye'd hurry faster if ye knew what I had outside for supper. What would a wee lad say, now, to a bit o' real Irish currant-bread, baked in the griddle, and a bowl of chicken broth with dumplings!"

—— *Ruth Sawyer*

Beggars Rhyme

Christmas is coming, the geese are getting fat,
Please to put a penny in the old man's hat;
If you haven't got a penny, a ha' penny will do.
If you haven't got a ha' penny, God bless you.
——*Nursery Rhyme*

Christmas in Provence

LITTLE TONINO and his sister lived in Nouvilo in the South of France. They lived with Papo, their father, Mamo, their mother, and Mameto, who was their grandmother. There were many pets in the household. Little Tonino had a donkey all his own, a donkey named Tintourlet.

Tonino loved to model in clay. One day not long before Christmas he made a model of Tintourlet and of Lavanda, the goat. Then he had an idea. He said to his little sister:

"Nanou, we won't show anything that I have made this afternoon to anybody. We will keep it a big secret, and next week when the figures are dry we will paint them and then we will set them up with all Mameto's little santons for the creche at Christmas. And won't they all be surprised!"

Adapted by Alice Dalgliesh from *Little Tonino,* by Helen Hill and Violet Maxwell; copyright, 1928, by The Macmillan Company; reprinted by permission.

Now I must explain exactly what a santon is. In the land of Provence, where Tonino and Nanou lived, it has been the custom for hundreds and hundreds of years for every family, at Christmas time, to make a creche (you pronounce this, kresh), which is a model of the stable in Bethlehem where Christ was born. All the churches have a creche in a side aisle at Christmas time, and this is sometimes very elaborate and wonderful. In Provence every family makes one all for itself too, and sets it up in the corner of the kitchen or living room.

Besides the figures of the Holy Family and the shepherds and the kings and the wise men bringing their gifts, the people of Provence have in their creches any number of other little figures bringing gifts to the Christ Child. There are peasants with loads of hay on their backs, women carrying water jars, hunters with their little guns, fishermen fishing in the brook, little schoolboys and little schoolgirls, old ladies with their sticks and young ones with spinning wheels—in fact, I could not begin to tell you one-quarter of all the fascinating little figures that the Provencal people set up in their creches. These little clay figures are called santons, and of course no family could have them all; some are very old and they are seen only at Christmas time and then packed very carefully away. But if any do get broken one can buy new ones at Christmas time, for in every village a peddler comes around and sets up his booth in the market place, filled with hundreds of little santons.

Tonino's grandmother had a box full of santons, in fact I think that the creche that she made at Christmas had more santons than any other in the village. Some of her santons were very old; they had been given to her by her grandmother and her grandmother had given them to her, and very likely her grandmother had passed them on to her! Some of Mameto's santons were more than a hundred years old, yet only one had ever been broken, and that was the black king!

It had happened only the Christmas before. What made it especially sad was that when Tonino's grandmother went to the peddler's booth to buy a new black king, there were not any more left. So this Christmas Eve there would be no black king with scarlet mantle, bringing gifts to the Christ Child.

It was of this that Nanou suddenly thought when she saw the beautiful figures that Tonino could make out of his big lump of clay. She said, "Oh, Tonino, let me have a little piece of clay and see if I can make a black king for the creche instead of the one that was broken last year. Wouldn't that surprise them all?"

So she took a piece of clay and she pinched and smoothed and rolled it; but alas and alack, Nanou did not have the potter's touch, and try as she would she could not make her piece of clay look like a king or indeed anything at all. Then she said: "Oh, Tonino, I can't do it at all. You try."

But Tonino said: "I don't think I could do it either without looking at the figures of the other kings. I'll tell you what I'll do; I'll ask Mameto to lend me the santon of the king with the golden crown, and I'll make the black king exactly like him, only we'll paint his cloak scarlet instead of purple and I'll make him a turban as well as a crown."

Then he looked out of the window and said:
"Why, there are Papo and Mamo and Mameto coming

toward the house, and it's beginning to get dark. I didn't think we had been working so long. Let's find a hiding place for Tintourlet and Lavanda where they will get dry and where Papo and Mamo and Mameto won't find them."

Nanou found a beautiful hiding place, on a little shelf above the window that neither she nor Tonino had known was there before. She climbed onto a chair and put the little figures of Tintourlet and Lavanda very carefully side by side on the shelf. They only had time to pull the chair away and rush to the other side of the room and pretend to be examining a spot on the wall, when their father and mother and grandmother came in, all ready to admire the beautiful things that Tonino had been making with his lump of clay.

The next morning was Sunday and Papo and Mamo went to church. When they had gone Tonino begged Mameto to lend him the santon of the king with the golden crown. He promised to be ever so careful of it. He did not tell Mameto why he wanted it and she did not ask him any questions, but went to her wedding chest, where she kept all her treasures, unlocked it, and handed Tonino the little santon. Tonino took the king back to the kitchen and got out a little lump of clay and tried to make a little figure just like it.

Instead of the crown he planned to make a turban, as the Moorish king always wears a turban. He found it was more difficult than he had expected. He had to squeeze up the clay and try again and again before he was satisfied. But at last he made a little figure that pleased him very much, which looked exactly like a tiny man in a long cloak with a turban on his head.

Already he had a new idea. He took a little lump of clay and the green water pitcher and he ran up to his mother's room, where there was a looking-glass. He climbed up on a chair so that he could see himself from head to foot in the looking-glass, and he put the water pitcher on his head and held it there with one hand, and looked at himself very hard. Then he put the pitcher down and he molded the clay and made a little figure of a boy carrying a water pitcher on his head. Of course it was the figure of the little water carrier in the story about Citronella.

He had just finished when he heard Nanou running up the stairs; and when she saw what Tonino had done she was astonished. She could not believe that he had made them all by himself. Suzetto had promised to let them use her paints one day soon, but the figures, she had told Nanou, must be quite dry before they could be painted. They must wait for several days.

Tonino and Nanou thought the time would never come. At last all the little clay figures were dry, and one afternoon at the end of the week they climbed the staircase that led to Suzetto's kitchen. They found her putting the finishing touches to a bowl she was decorating with a little white house with a red roof and a pine tree growing beside it.

Suzetto's table was drawn up close to the window and her saucers of paint were in a row in front of her, white paint and red and blue and yellow and green and a lovely shade of purple. On a shelf, beside the window and easy to reach from her table, were the cups and saucers and bowls and salt-cellars that she had finished painting that day. Some of them were painted only with a coat of white, which must dry before Suzetto could paint the little flowers and garlands around it.

Tonino and Nanou admired them all, but the one that Tonino liked best was the bowl with the little house and green trees painted on it. He was afraid that he would never be able to paint as beautifully as that. But, when Tonino and Nanou opened their package, it was Suzetto's turn to admire and she was amazed at the little figures that Tonino had made. Of course Suzetto would have loved to paint them herself, but she knew that it was Tonino's right as he had made them.

So Tonino sat down in Suzetto's chair and filled his brush with gray paint and proceeded to paint Tintourlet gray; he painted him all gray except for his nose which he painted white, and then he tried to put in his eyes. But alas and alack, he could not get Tintourlet's eyes in the right place; the first time he tried he put one eye up near Tintourlet's ear and the other close to his nose! So he painted them out and tried again, but with no better success.

All this time Nanou had been watching and longing to get the paint brush in her hands, and now she said: "Oh, Tonino, do let me try. I'd like to help to earn the money to keep Tintourlet, and I know that I could paint his eyes beautifully. I painted a picture of a donkey last week in school and the teacher said mine was the best of all. Please let me try, Tonino!"

So Tonino did let her try and Nanou sat down and filled a very fine brush with brown paint, and she put out her tongue a little way and gave one tiny dab with the brush, and then another and behold Tintourlet had two beautiful brown eyes in exactly the right place. Then, after washing her brush clean, she took some red paint and painted his red bridle; and, when she had painted the grass he was standing on a bright green, the figure of Tintourlet was complete.

Tonino was delighted. He was so delighted that he allowed Nanou to paint the water carrier; and she was just as successful with the water carrier. She painted his pitcher and the grass green and she gave him a red cap and a red sash, and made his shirt white and his hair and breeches black. His hands and face, of course, were pink. Last of all she put two little black dots for his eyes and a little red dot for his mouth.

Then Suzetto was allowed to paint Lavanda and of course she did it beautifully. She painted her white, just like Lavanda, with black spots and dear little black hoofs. Last of all Tonino painted the black king. He painted his coat with the beautiful purple paint, his turban white, his face a dark brown, but it was Nanou who painted his eyes and his black beard.

Now all the figures were painted and Suzetto suggested that they put them on her shelf with all her other pottery to dry. Tonino and Nanou thought this a very good plan, especially when Nanou said, "Let's leave them there till Christmas Eve, if Suzetto will let us, and not say a word to any one at home. Then when the creche is all ready Tonino can run over and get the figures and we'll slip them in among the other santons and see how surprised they'll all be when they notice that there is a new black king and three other new santons!"

Not so very long after that it was Christmas Eve. Mamo and Mameto had been growing corn and grass seed in flat dishes to decorate the creche, and to make a grassy meadow for it. After dinner Tonino's father brought up a big packing-case, and placed it in the corner between the window and the fireplace. Mamo got a green cloth and covered the box so that the folds fell over the sides of the packing-case to the floor. Then Mameto went to her wedding chest and brought out the santons. She also brought out the little stable, which was made of wood and which had a roof made of corrugated cardboard painted red to look like the tiled roofs in Nouvilo, only the tiled roofs in Nouvilo have all turned gray with age.

In front of the stable she put the green meadow, and at the side the dish with the tall blades of corn; then she arranged the moss and the stones that Tonino and Nanou had collected, so that the sides of the tin and the dish were quite hidden. At the back of the stable she arranged all the tiny trees with more rocks and moss, so that it looked as if the stable were built on the edge of a wooded cliff with a green meadow in front.

When Mameto had finished arranging all the santons you have no idea how beautiful it looked. In the stable she put the Holy family, with the Christ Child lying in his manger and a donkey and two cows near him. Then on the grassy meadow she arranged the shepherd santon with his sheep, the hunter and the woodcutter and the gypsy lass, and the washerwoman and others coming through the corn fields.

There were the knife grinder and the spinner and the gardener and so many peasant santons, some carrying baskets of fruit on their heads or bundles of firewood or casks of olive oil. Even the fisherman was not forgotten; there he sat beside a pool at the edge of the wood with his fishing line, and the pool was made of a little round mirror that belonged to Nanou.

On the highest tree behind the stable Mameto pinned a golden star, and in front of the creche she arranged four candles in pottery candlesticks. Now all the santons were in their place except the kings, but these would not arrive until the Feast of Kings, which is on the sixth of January. So Mameto put them at the very edge of the table right by the candlesticks, and she would move them forward a little every day until on the Feast of Kings they would be standing near the stable to present their gifts.

As Mameto looked at them she said: "It is too bad that the Moorish King is broken. I have never seen a creche where there were only two kings. If it had been another king I might have put another santon in his place, but the Moorish King is the only one that has a brown face."

Tonino and Nanou looked at each other and found it difficult not to laugh, for they had the new santons that Tonino had made all ready in their pockets. At last Papo said, "Well, I must be going to milk Lavanda." Mamo said, "I will put on a pretty dress in honor of the creche." Mameto began to prepare the vegetables for supper. The very moment that her back was turned Tonino slipped over to the table and put Tintourlet and Lavanda and the water carrier beside the shepherd in the grassy meadow. As for the Moorish King he put him beside the other two kings on the edge of the table and only just in time, for Mameto turned around and told him not to meddle with the creche.

But she did not notice anything, though she passed quite close to the table when she went to get the butter from the window cupboard. After supper, however, when the candles in front of the creche were lighted, Mameto suddenly said: "Who moved the donkey from the stable and put it among the shepherds—and who put the goat among the sheep? And where did this figure of a little water carrier come from?" Then at last she saw the Moorish King and she said: "Why, it is a miracle! Here are three kings where I put only two, and one is like the Moorish King that was broken last year!"

She looked at Tonino and Nanou—and the secret was out! You may believe that their Papo and Mamo were delighted to know that Tonino had made such beautiful figures with his lump of clay and that Nanou had painted them so beautifully.

Then Tonino and Nanou recited the little prayer that all Provencal children learn to say in front of the creche at Christmas:

"Teach us, Holy Child, we ask,
Cheerfully to do our task.
Make us love to delve and toil
Like the tiller of the soil,
Like the oxen, strong and steady,
Like the watchman, ever ready.
Make us like the shepherd, wise
To know the warnings in the skies.
Make us patient as the ass,
Merry as the gypsy lass,
Like the potter at his wheel
For his handcraft full of zeal."

There are more verses than we can print, and Tonino and Nanou did not know them all either, as there is one for every figure in the creche and it would need another book to print them all. But Tonino never forgot to say the verse about the potter.

Before they went to bed, instead of hanging up their stockings, they left their shoes on the hearthstone for Papo Noël to fill with presents. The next morning, when Tonino and Nanou came tiptoeing down to see their presents they found their shoes full of little toys and candy and nuts. Beside their old shoes they each found a pair of straw sabots lined with rabbit fur.

——*Helen Hill and Violet Maxwell*

Christmas Carol

The Kings they came from out the South,
    All dressed in ermine fine;
They bore Him gold and chrysophrase,
    And gifts of precious wine.

The Shepherds came from out the North,
    Their coats were brown and old:
They brought Him little new-born lambs—
    They had not any gold.

The Wise Men came from out the East,
    And they were wrapped in white:
The star that led them all the way
    Did glorify the night.

The Angels came from heaven high,
    And they were clad with wings:
And lo they brought a joyful song
    The host of heaven sings.

The Kings they knocked upon the door,
    The Wise Men entered in,
The Shepherds followed after them
    To hear the song begin.

The Angels sang through all the night
    Until the rising sun,
But little Jesus fell asleep
    Before the song was done.

        ——*Sara Teasdale*

"Christmas Carol" is from *Helen of Troy and Other Poems*, by Sara Teasdale; copyright, 1922, by The Macmillan Company; reprinted by permission.

A Star for Hansi

SOPHIE IS A FRIENDLY NAME. You cannot think
that a little girl to whom it belonged would sulk, or refuse
to answer to "How do you do?" or take the largest currant
muffin.

Sophie Ebbert, who lived in the large, lemon-colored
house behind the very high green hedge, was just the
little girl to be called by a friendly name. Her eyes were
gray, and a dimple near the corner of the left one gave to
her face when she smiled what Grosmutter called her
"twinkly look." When Sophie smiled—and she did very
often—you thought of hidden fairy lights shining from
those merry twinkly eyes. Sophie's cheeks were red and
round as snow apples, and her brown hair, in two neat,
short pigtails, bobbed across her shoulders.

Sometimes they were tied with blue ribbons, and sometimes with red, but on important days, or when there were guests, plaid ribbons, red and blue and gold all together, finished the ends of the fat brown braids.

One of the things that always made Sophie happy was that her birthday—and this time it had been her eighth—came just a week before Christmas when one was growing a little impatient for the great day itself to come. A birthday, though not so important, did a great deal to make a pleasant break in the time of waiting.

Today, however, was one of the very rare times when the "twinkly look" was gone and even the brave plaid bows on her braids drooped.

It was Sunday afternoon. Snow drifted softly down on the garden. The bushes looked like huge white frosted cakes, the pine trees like the sugar trees in the candy shops, which would stand on Christmas dinner tables next week. Inside, the lamps had not been lighted, but from the hearth a pink warm light stole out to touch the edges of things. Sophie watched the white snowflakes lose themselves in the gray twilight, and sighed. Grosmutter closed her book and lighted the lamp—the one with the pink china shade. Then she came and stood beside Sophie.

"What is it, Liebchen?" she asked. "You are quiet today and just now you sighed much too deeply for a little girl just halfway between her birthday party and Christmas. What is it?"

"Nothing—" began Sophie, and then, before she could stop them, big tears were sliding down her cheeks and Grosmutter was wiping them with her handkerchief which smelled of lavender and spice.

"Come, come, tell me what is troubling you, little child. Maybe I can help. Here on my lap—come."

She drew Sophie onto her lap and listened while the little story was told.

"I had saved my allowance to buy Mother and Father and you and Peter Christmas gifts," she began. "I got Peter's boat, and Father's pencil, and—and your gift. The man in the perfume shop has a little bottle shaped like a green lantern. It is filled with the cologne Mother likes. He is saving it for me. I had enough money to buy it, and Father was going to take me to town tomorrow afternoon to get it—and now—" Sophie's voice trailed off and stopped.

"And now what?"

"Well—you see when Karen came for my party last week we went to the village and—I—I spent all I had left for gingerbread men, and now—" Again the big tears began to slip down Sophie's cheeks.

Grosmutter looked grave, even with the pink lamp and the firelight making everything so warm and friendly.

"So you spent all your money on gingerbread men," she said. "Ach, that is bad, little Sophie, very bad. Now, now, don't cry so!" for now the tears were coming faster and faster. "See, I shall tell you the story of the applewood box. Would you like that?"

Sophie nodded.

"What did it look like?" she asked.

"It was round—round as a chestnut, and just that color. Now listen well.

"Once long ago there stood on the edge of the great Black Forest a beautiful castle. Around it spread its parks where deer and antelope walked softly through the speckled shadows. Beyond the park was the hamlet where lived the people who served the baron of the castle. In their little cottages they lived—woodcutters, shepherds, farmers, the blacksmith, shopkeepers, the school-teacher, the pastor, the bürgermeister.

"In the little house of the bürgermeister besides himself, there lived his wife and their three children, Tomas, little Hans, and a little girl about your age. And what do you suppose her name was?"

Sophie shook her head, and almost the dimple peeped out.

"I don't know. What was it?"

"Sophie."

"Sophie—like me?"

"Yes, Liebchen, very much like you. I think that other Sophie looked just a little like you, too. Tomas was two years older than his sister and four years older than little Hans.

"In all the Black Forest region there was no child just like little Hans. His hair was like pale sunshine caught and rolled into soft curls all over his head. His dark eyes seemed to see far-away places; and when little Hans laughed Tomas put down his whittling and Sophie stopped her knitting the better to listen to so sweet a sound. Little Hans did not play their games, nor did he go with them to tend geese in the swamp. He sat and played quietly in a sunny spot where his chair was placed. Sometimes his father carried him into the woods and he called to the birds in his high sweet voice, by little names he made up for them.

"Sophie and Tomas and their parents all loved one another dearly, but their love for little Hans was quite different. It was as though there must be enough love for Hansi to remember forever and ever.

"Now, though the bürgermeister had his snug cottage, and though his family was clothed and fed, still he was not a rich man, and his children earned whatever they could to buy the little extra things that girls and boys like. Tomas helped the woodcutter gather the lighter branches as they fell under his ax and saw, and tied them in neat, tight bundles. On baking days, when his mother's loaves were ready to be carried to the village oven for baking, he stopped at the cottage of the blacksmith, the tailor, and the doctor, and carried the loaves their wives had set, too, and later returned each golden loaf, crusty and hot from the oven to its owner.

"Sophie crocheted fine lace for the linen pillowcases in the castle, and knitted worsted caps and mufflers for the children of the baron. Each morning when she drove her mother's geese to the swamp, she drove the geese of the miller and the storekeeper, too.

"For these little tasks the children received a few coppers. That is how Tomas came to own his jackknife for whittling, and how Sophie had the white knitting-needles with tiny roses and violets painted on them.

"One day in early autumn the school-teacher called Sophie to him and said:

" 'I have something here for you, Sophie, which I hope you will always treasure. Look, it was given me by my teacher when I was your age.'

"He put into Sophie's hands a small round box."

"Was it the applewood box, Grosmutter?"

"Yes, exactly, and this is what he said: 'This little box is only for a careful child, and I believe you are that,

There is a coin in it now. See that there is at least one coin, however small, in it at all times. There is only one exception to this rule. When your heart quite plainly says, "Now, now is the time to spend the last coin," then spend it gladly. Otherwise, remember, always keep at least one coin in the box. It will call in others. When you have grown to be an old lady search well for another careful child and pass the box on to him or her with this same advice.'

"So he gave the applewood box to the happy little girl, and—"

"And did it have a coin in it?"

"Yes, a pfennig; and Sophie promised that she would never let the little box be empty unless her heart quite plainly said, 'Now, now is the time to spend the last coin.'

"She was so proud of her new prize that she ran home through the woods and burst in on her mother, who was spinning beside the fire."

"What did Tomas and little Hans say?"

"Tomas was away in the woods with the woodcutter, but little Hans held the box against his cheek and laughed softly and said, 'It is smooth and cool like the moon.'

"The days flew and Sophie worked very diligently at all the tasks at home, at school, and at those other tasks which brought coins to the little box.

"One day a peddler came to the village with strange and beautiful toys from across the Russian border—little carved squirrels that climbed a string, small tops of many colors, music-boxes that played wild, sweet tunes that seemed to come from far-away lovely places behind the snowy sunset. Tomas selected a set of tops, spent his last coin, and grieved when evening came and his tops were

broken. Sophie knew that little Hans would have loved
a music-box, but as he had not seen ANY of the toys, she
carried the prettiest brown squirrel home to him instead
and shared his fun as he watched it run up and down
the string. In the applewood box there was still the last
coin to begin fresh saving for other useful and amusing
things.

"Again, when the family all went to the fair in the
early winter, Sophie was tempted. There was the man
selling cardamon cakes, another selling chocolate and herb
tea delicately spiced. In one tent a big black bear danced
and boxed with his trainer; in another a troupe of dwarfs
tumbled and did amusing tricks. Tomas spent his last coin,
poor lad, yet saw only half that he wanted. Sophie chose
a cardamon cake and saw the dancing bear, and went home
happy, with a cake for little Hans, and a coin still rattling
in the applewood box. More lace to be crocheted, more
cold mornings helping with the geese and chickens, and
soon there would be more coins to make a gay tinkling
in the box.

"Soon it was time for the lovely Christmas festival.
Mother baked pfeffernusse and springerlein until the little
cottage was sweet with spicy fragrance. Father brought
in fresh wood and laid pine cones between the kindling
to make a more snapping Christmas fire while he told the
children stories of other Christmases in the Black Forest.

"One evening he told the story of the first Christmas
and how a great, beautiful, silver star had led the way
to the Baby Jesus. Little Hans was in his arms, listening
to the story. His sunny hair made a great splash of gold
against his father's coat.

" 'Did they find Him, Father?' he asked.

" 'Of course,' Father answered; 'they just followed where the star led, and there at last they found the Child, and He held out His little arms to them.'

"The other children did not say anything, but little Hans smiled.

" 'That was nice,' he said, 'nice.'

"The next day was Christmas Eve, so Sophie and Tomas took their coins and went to the village, and what fun they had! A bit of beeswax for Mother's ironing-board, a new goose quill for Father's writing-pad, a jumping-jack and a stick of candy for little Hans. For each other they choose a collection of small things which, of course, they would not show until the tree was lighted after sunset. Hugging their packages, they ran home through the twilight, hoping Mother had not finished trimming the tree and placing the little manger beneath it."

"But, was it really, truly a manger, Grosmutter?"

"Yes, a tiny stable, and just inside, a manger filled with real hay for the Child Jesus to lie upon. And then grouped all around were the figures of Mary and Joseph and the wise men and shepherds—all made of wax.

"Tomas ran to hide his packages and Sophie threw off her hood and cape and went to little Hans. He was not in his chair by the window this evening, but in his little bed, for he was tired. So Sophie put the lumpy jumping-jack in its brown wrapping on the bed beside him.

" 'Guess what Sophie brought for you, Hansi,' she said, and waited while his fingers moved over the stiff paper. Never, never would he guess!

"Is it—Sophie, is it—a star?" he whispered at last, and his own dark eyes were like stars.

"Sophie's heart sank. A jumping-jack! and he had

wanted a star! For a few pfennigs a beautiful star, all shimmering and silvery white, could be had in a shop at the other end of the village! But she had spent all her money—all but—! Suddenly Sophie straightened up. There was that last coin which must never be touched unless quite plainly her heart said, 'Now, now is the time to spend the last coin,' and now her heart spoke.

"She smiled down at little Hans, and he smiled happily back.

" 'Is it—is it truly a star?' he asked again, very softly.

"Sophie kissed his fingers resting on the package.

" 'Just you wait, Hansi, until Sophie comes back,' she whispered, and taking the jumping-jack, she ran to the woodshed where Tomas was helping Father with the little tree for which Mother was clearing a space on the table.

" 'Hide this with your other things, Tomas,' she said. 'I'm going to run back to the village. I'll not be gone long —I'll hurry.'

"She threw on her cape, and holding the applewood box tightly, ran through the woods to the village, thinking she never had heard anything more comforting than the sound of the coin rattling away merrily in the little box as she ran. The shopkeeper smiled at her serious face.

" 'A star for little Hansi, eh?' he exclaimed. Together they looked over the rows of beautiful white-and-silver stars hanging like a sparkling girdle around the shop walls, and at last the shopkeeper took down the shiniest one he had and held it out to her.

" 'There,' he said, 'there is the brightest star in the shop, and little Hans is just the child it was meant to shine for. Be sure to wish him a good Christmas for me, eh?'

"Sophie gave him her last coin happily, and holding

the star carefully under her cape, sped back over the snow
to the cottage at the edge of the wood.

"Now the sun had set and from the windows of the
bürgermeister's little house a warm welcoming light
streamed out, making a gay pattern on the snow.

" 'The whole house seems to glow,' thought Sophie,
hurrying toward it, 'as though it were full of lovely
stars!'

"Softly she opened the door, and softly—not knowing
why—hurried through the passage. At the door of the
family room she stopped. There was a hush in the room—
as when a bird stops singing or a bubbling fountain ceases
to play.

"The little tree standing on the table shone quietly in
the soft white light of its candles. Before it, all together,
was the family—Mother, Father, Tomas, and in Father's
arms little Hans. Mother knelt beside Father's chair, with
her cheek against Hansi's curls, and Sophie could see
that she had forgotten Father and Tomas and even Christmas—everything but little Hans. Father was telling the
Christmas story again, very slowly, very carefully, so that
even if one were tired and drowsy, still one could hear
and understand.

" 'They followed where the star led,' Father said, 'and
there at last—'

"Little Hans opened his eyes. He saw Sophie. He
smiled all over his little face.

" 'Look, Hansi,' she whispered, and slid to her knees
before Father's chair and held up the great quivering
silver star.

" 'For me! For me!' the little boy said, softly, and held
out his hands and laughed; and looking at his Christmas

star, he fell asleep there before the Baby Christ in the manger who held out His little arms to him. And Sophie knew she had done well to take the last coin from the applewood box. And that is the end of the story, Lieb-chen."

Sophie stirred.

"Tell some more," she begged. "Did little Hans wake up after a while and see his star again? and did Sophie grow up? and what did she do with the box?"

Grosmutter smiled gently.

"Little Hans woke up—yes, and never was tired any more. Sophie grew up, and what do you suppose she did with the applewood box? Jump down, dear; I am going to show you something."

Grosmutter went to her room, and in a moment she was back, carrying a small object in her hands.

"This is from one Sophie to another," she said, smiling —"to you."

Sophie could not believe her eyes, for there in her hands was a small, round, dark box of polished wood!

"Is it—oh, Grosmutter, IS IT THE APPLEWOOD BOX?" Sophie's dimple was back and so was the "twinkly look."

Grosmutter nodded.

"Then are you—were you—that Sophie?"

Again Grosmutter nodded, or tried to, because Sophie's arms were around her neck in a bear hug, and her flushed round cheek pressed so tightly to Grosmutter's that she scarcely could move.

"Oh, it was the loveliest, LOVELIEST story, Gros-mutter!" she said, "and I'll be so proud of my box!"

"Then see, child; let us open it."

Carefully Sophie took off the polished lid. The box was quite filled with coins.

"Now then," Grosmutter asked, "how much shall we need to buy the lantern filled with cologne?"

Sophie's dimple disappeared.

"Fifty cents," she answered, and just saying it made it sound twice as much.

Grosmutter emptied the coins on the table and together they counted them.

"Just exactly fifty pennies!" Grosmutter beamed. Sophie shrieked with glee.

"Goody! Goody!" she cried. "Now in the morning the first thing Father and I can go to town and buy the lantern! Fifty cents is exactly what I needed and now I have it! I'm so happy! So happy!" She danced around the room. Then suddenly she noticed that Grosmutter was looking at her a little strangely, a little sadly.

"I am afraid," she said, "that my little Sophie does not remember the most important part of all in the story of the box. What about the last coin?"

Sophie stopped short in her dance.

"Oh—I forgot," she said—"I forgot."

"When does Father give you your next allowance?"

"Tomorrow. Peter and I get it every Monday morning."

"Well, then—?"

"Oh, I see!" The dimple came twinkling out again. "I see! Look, Grosmutter, I'll leave five pennies instead of only one in the box. That will leave forty-five pennies I can keep out. Then tomorrow I'll add five pennies from my allowance, and that will give me enough to buy the lantern and still leave coins in the box to 'call in others,' as the school-teacher said when he gave the box to So—I mean to you."

Grosmutter patted her cheek.

"That is my little Sophie," she said. "That is being a 'careful child,' a worthy owner of the applewood box."

So on Christmas Eve, tucked in her snug bed, Sophie thought happily of Mother's cologne lantern hanging bravely on the tree downstairs. Above, the Christmas stars shone softly down, and one, larger, brighter than the others, she thought must look very like the one the other Sophie had brought to little Hans on that long-ago Christmas Eve in the Black Forest. As she drifted into happy Christmas dreams she made a solemn promise always to guard her last coin carefully, but to spend it gladly, thankfully when her heart quite plainly said, "Now, now is the time."

—*Marguerite Vance*

Gates and Doors

There was a gentle hostler
  (And blessed be his name!)
He opened up the stable
  The night Our Lady came.
Our Lady and Saint Joseph,
  He gave them food and bed,
And Jesus Christ has found him
  A glory round his head.

So let the gate swing open
  However poor the yard,
Lest weary people visit you
  And find their passage barred;
Unlatch the door at midnight
  And let your lanterns glow
Shine out to guide the traveler's feet
  To you across the snow.

There was a courteous hostler
  (He is in heaven tonight.)
He held Our Lady's bridle
  And helped her to alight;
He spread clean straw before her
  Whereon she might lie down,
And Jesus Christ has given him
  An everlasting crown.

Unlock the door this evening
   And let your gate swing wide,
Let all who ask for shelter
   Come speedily inside.
What if your yard be narrow?
   What if your house be small?
There is a guest is coming
   Will glorify it all.

There was a joyous hostler
   Who knelt on Christmas morn
Beside the radiant manger
   Wherein his Lord was born.
His heart was full of laughter,
   His soul was full of bliss
When Jesus, on His Mother's lap,
   Gave him His hand to kiss.

Unlock your heart this evening
   And keep no stranger out,
Take from your soul's great portal
   The barrier of doubt.
To humble folk and weary
   Give hearty welcoming
Your breast shall be tomorrow
   The cradle of a King.
                    ——*Joyce Kilmer*

Christmas Eve in the Tyrol

"CHRISTMAS EVE," thought Hansi, "should start with the evening. There should be no day on that day at all."

Certainly it was the biggest day in the year and the longest to wait around in.

He was sent from the house on errands as soon as he came in. Packages wandered around. One room was locked and even the keyhole stuffed so one could see nothing.

The children weren't hungry though there were the most wonderful things on the table.

"Hansi, nothing is going to happen until this plate is empty. Lieserl, stop wiggling on that chair." Uncle Herman finally looked at his watch and got up. Soon a

---

little silver bell rang, and sparkling across the hall stood the Christmas tree. It turned slowly to music, as glass angels, cookies and burning candles rode around.

The best skis in the whole world are made of Norwegian spruce with long tapered ends. Such a pair stood beside the tree—new and with a binding like that the champion jumpers use. Next to them a skiing cap with a long tassel. Aunt Amalie had knitted it for Hansi. The skis, of course, were from his mother. Uncle Herman had given Hansi a skiing jacket, bright red and warm so that one could get lost and yet stay warm and easily be found in the white snow.

Lieserl had a doll carriage with a big doll dressed like a peasant girl on Sunday. This doll could go to sleep and even said, "Mama," when she was pinched.

"Yes, Lieserl, I see," said Hansi, and looked at his skis again.

Hansi had barely slipped into the skis to try them on and put the stocking cap on his head, when singing was heard outside the house.

"Here they are," said Uncle Herman. Everybody tiptoed to the door, and quietly it swung open.

Three Kings stood majestically in the starry night and sang in verses. They told how they had come from the sands of the desert and were passing this house on the way to visit the Christ Kinderl, to offer Him their precious gifts. Long heavy robes of scarlet flowed off them into the snow. Over their serious devout faces shone tall crowns of pure gold. Their hands were hidden in the deep folds of scarlet sleeves and one of them held a silver lance on which shone the star that had guided the Kings from the East past this house.

After they had finished their song, Uncle Herman invited them to enter his home. He did so singing a verse to which they answered with singing and came in.

Aunt Amalie had brought three cups of hot chocolate and a big plate of Lebkuchen. The Kings seemed to be very hungry indeed after the hard trip from the hot desert and over the cold mountains. Each took three Lebkuchen as they sat down, falling over the plate in their hurry to reach it. One Lebkuchen was left and, as one of the Kings tried to reach for it, the biggest one hit him on the fingers with the silver lance to which was attached the morning star, which broke off and fell into the chocolate. Uncle Herman seemed to know these Kings very well. He took the lances away from them so they would not hurt each other any more.

Lieserl sat down next to the smallest King, who was black and looked at him very closely. Then she wet her finger and rubbed his nose. The King started to cry and his nose turned white.

"I knew it all the time," said Lieserl. "It's Frau Kofler's little boy Peterl."

Now Hansi came to the table, and he could see that the King, outside of a black face, had only black fingernails. His hands were white—almost white. They were boys from the village. The beautiful stars and crowns were made with gold and silver paper pasted over it and the little King was blackened with burnt cork.

They had to sing at three more houses, they said. Aunt Amalie brought two more Lebkuchens, so each could eat another, and Uncle Herman repaired the little King's pale nose with stove blacking. They gave thanks with a little verse for the shelter and food and bowed and walked back into the night. The cold light of the moon gave them back their lost majesty. As they left everyone was serious and quiet. Their stars and crowns had turned again to purest beaten gold.

The evening passed as quickly as the day had been slow in going. Soon it was time to go to midnight services.

This was one of three days in the year when Uncle Herman stood in front of a mirror. He buttoned his tunic and pinned his medals on according to regulation, "six fingers down from the seam of the collar, three fingers over from the second button—right over the heart." Belt and saber were adjusted carefully. Uncle Herman breathed on the buckle and polished it with his sleeve.

Aunt Amalie said, "Why don't you ask for a piece of cloth? It's a shame—the nice new uniform."

The feathers on the green huntsman's hat were straightened out, the white gloves put on.

The children looked up in awe at their new uncle who looked like a picture of his old emperor.

Aunt Amalie had her best dress on with a wide silk shawl around her shoulders and silver lacing from which jingled thalers as she walked.

Hansi and Lieserl sat around like pictures painted on the wall. They had been ready for an hour, and held the little lanterns that were used to light the way down the path.

Aunt Amalie put some things on the table for a small supper when they came back.

The night helped to make Christmas. All the stars were out. The windows of the mountain church shone out into the blue night from the valley and from high up little rows of lights came towards the church. People carried them. They shone up into happy, quiet faces. Silent night, holy night—only the bells of the churches rang from near and from the far white fields.

They scraped the snow from their shoes and entered the church. It smelled like a cool forest at noontime when the sun shines through the tall pines. Pines stood in rows along the walls reaching almost to the tower. Candles flickered everywhere.

Hansi walked up the creaky stairway that led through the tower and opened into the choir. A big oil lamp hung over the organ that was built a century ago. In front of it sat the village schoolmaster. He gave Hansi notes and nodded to the place where he was to stand with other boys. Behind him a man was tuning two large copper kettledrums. He bent his ear close to them and struck them with a softly padded hammer. It was a lovely warm sound that made Hansi feel hollow inside.

Post Seppl was up here with a trumpet, and there were the players of two more instruments—a flute and a fiddle.

In front of the organ above the schoolmaster's head was a little mirror. In this the teacher watched the services. He could tell when to play, and he kept the time by nodding his head.

The church below was filled to the doors with kindly people who thanked God for their beautiful mountains and asked no more of Him than that He keep them as He had all the years of their plain good lives.

The old teacher lifted his eyes and asked in addition for His help in repairing this poor tired organ. Not only were many important sounds missing—there were others that did not make melodies, and of the two wooden angels that flew to left and right of it, one needed his robe painted and the other had lost a wing.

After services Uncle Herman waited below with Aunt Amalie and Lieserl for Hansi. They went home together as they had come, with other little lights that wandered from the church to the houses on the mountain.

——*Ludwig Bemelmans*

As Joseph Was a-Walking

As Joseph was a-walking
  He heard an angel sing,
"This night shall be the birth-time
  Of Christ, the Heavenly King.

He neither shall be born
  In house nor in hall,
Nor in a place of paradise,
  But in an ox's stall.

He shall not be clothèd
  In purple nor in pall;
But in the fair white linen,
  That usen babies all.

He neither shall be rockèd
  In silver nor in gold,
But in a wooden manger
  That resteth on the mold."

As Joseph was a-walking
  There did an angel sing,
And Mary's child at midnight
  Was born to be our King.

Then be ye glad, good people,
  This night of all the year,
And light ye up your candles,
  For His star it shineth clear.
          —*Old English*

Dobry's Christmas

THE INTENSE COLD changed to a thaw and the villagers were able to open their snow tunnels into roads before Christmas. Then a quick freeze left the snow dry with a hard icy crust.

Because she was motherless, Neda and her shoemaker father always spent Christmas Eve at Dobry's home. Roda being maternal enough for two peasant women, had years ago made Neda's coming a habit.

Their supper on Christmas Eve was eaten earlier than usual. At twilight they sat down to the simplest meal imaginable, because the forty-day fast in preparation for the Christmas feast was never broken until after midnight mass. A suckling pig roasted under hot ashes in the jamal,

Christmas breads were browning in the kitchen oven, the whole house smelled of temptation—yet supper tonight was only boiled-up fruits the family had harvested and dried. Fruit soup, they called it, and ate this Christmas Eve soup with bread, torn from a special loaf Roda had baked with a very old silver coin in the middle, the Christ Child's gift to the finder—a benediction.

Hristu crumbled up piece after piece of bread, impatient for the good-luck piece, but Dobry, eating a hunk of the bread, bit on the lucky old coin. "I nearly swallowed my good luck and my blessing!" he cried. He polished his luck on his blouse, showed it to Neda as if the world had no other coin like this one, and put the lucky blessing away in his sash.

Grandfather said to him, "Last year I got the Christmas coin, and you saw me—I won the Snow-Melting Game! And I still feel myself as lucky as a stork." He laughed. "Just having me here should bring luck to the house." He shook his head at Dobry. "Good Luck!" he roared.

But Hristu's face sagged and he thought, "No, Roda will never marry me. I'm a good-enough shoemaker, but I have no luck." He said out loud, "I never get the lucky coin—never. Not once in my life!"

Neda put her hand on his arm. "I know," she said. But Grandfather interrupted her sympathy and told the shoemaker:

"You are always too anxious, Hristu. Every Christmas Eve you take a hunk of bread, crumble it, take another hunk of bread, crumble it without eating. You are too anxious. And a too anxious person bites his own tongue, sticks his finger in his own eye, trips himself up, and misses his luck altogether. If you hold a wish too tight it can't fly, any more than a stork can fly if you hold him tight. Just enjoy your bread and some day, without knowing how, you'll bite right into luck, Hristu—the way Dobry did just now."

Dark came long before they had done talking and laughing at table. "Time to go out to the animals," Dobry said, getting up and lighting a candle for each one to take along. For on Christmas Eve, between night and morning, every Bulgarian peasant takes up a lighted candle, goes out, and wakes up each family animal, and says to him or her:

"The Child is born and blesses you tonight."

The head of the family takes with him a small earthen pot of incense, holds it under the nose of cow, pig, buffalo, ox, and lets each animal have a sniff. Dobry had often climbed the tallest pine in his mother's forest on Christmas Eve and watched candles all over the village going to and back from the barns and pens. But tonight his mind and spirit were both too absorbed in the dream he had mentioned to Neda—a dream alive in him but not yet sculptured.

After Sari and Pernik, the family pig and chickens, had been awakened and told, Neda left with her father to wake up Peter and the buffaloes, let them know that it was Christmas Eve, stroke them, thank them, and give them their blessing and sniff of incense.

"I'll come and get you for midnight mass. I'll come early," Dobry told Neda before she left.

And because anticipation breeds impatience, they set off too early for midnight mass, each carrying a lighted candle.

Their village church topped a hill and on the way up Dobry stopped climbing, and said to Neda:

"I like to be outside when the chimes ring, don't you? Bells sound dull, don't mean anything much once you're in the church."

Above them windows of the big low church lighted up, candle by candle, as altar boys hurried about inside. When all its candles burned, the village church became a symbol of Light, a star at the top of a hill. And below Dobry and Neda the village bobbed with candles, because every peasant—except the Pomak coppersmiths, father and son—was on his way to midnight mass.

Stars looked dimmer, much higher than usual. The moon, cloud muffled, could have been a reflection of the lighted church and the stars only reflections of the lighted candles bobbing now on every side of Dobry and Neda.

"Don't you wish we could believe in the Christmas bird the way we used to believe?" Neda questioned him. "Don't you remember? We used to put big sheets of paper out under our eaves, wake up on Christmas morning, run out barefooted to find our paper piled high with raisins and nuts and little Christmas breads. All dropped down by the Christmas bird."

Dobry said, "An enormous white bird! Flying down from the North. Son of a Wind bird and a giant Snow bird. I never believe in him on any night in the year except on Christmas Eve. I believe in any beautiful thing tonight. That's why I know the Christmas bird will come flying over the village before morning, a gunny sack of nuts and raisins in his beak. If the north sky opened now —and it might—the Christmas bird would fly straight over our heads on his way down to the village. But if he

did fly down over our heads the Christmas bird couldn't
make me jump. Tonight is a wonder. Nothing less could
startle me."

Chimes rang out and Grandfather, Roda, and Hristu
climbed the hill and pushed on with the crowd of people
roaring out greetings to each other before they stamped
into the church. Only Dobry and Neda waited outside
until the bells stopped ringing.

Everybody stood through the long Byzantine ritual, but
not stiffly. To these peasants their church was the hearth
of God and they made themselves at home, moved about,
nodded, spoke quietly to each other, or called out Christmas greetings with their eyes and their wide smiles. Dobry
pulled down a corner of his sash and whispered to Neda:

"Look, my good luck and my blessing. That means you
love me. Now I don't have to ask you, 'Neda, do you
love me?' Perfect!"

Neda said, "But look what you've done! If you show
your lucky piece in a church don't you know it loses everything—luck, benediction, everything—becomes just a coin
again. Didn't you know that? And if you call me a liar
in church that will be worse for you."

"But I can wait until after church." Dobry laughed,
held down the corner of one eye with his finger, and then
lost himself in the music.

Husky male voices sang the Christmas canon of Saint
John Damascene, greatest poet of the Eastern Church.
Without an instrument of any kind, peasants stood at each
side of the sanctuary's front and chanted in answer to each
other, every man expressing his quickened feelings, his
child-like wonder.

And to Dobry it all seemed as old, as mysterious as the

night outside did with its symbols of God. He said no prayers in words but his mind and his heart seemed to be on fire. Longing to do perfectly what he hoped to do grew into a desire strong enough to shake him and set his blood pounding. The priest in golden vestments and tall black hat, altar boys, their white banded by Mary's blue, seemed to Dobry like people in a dream and his own dream seemed real and urgent.

It was snowing when he came out of the church, surprised to find himself alone, not realizing that the others had left before him.

Neda had hurried off with Roda, intent on helping her prepare the Feast of Sparrows. But they found Grandfather home before them, keeping up the jamal fire which roasted their suckling pig. Dobry had saved out the biggest log he had felled that winter, rolled it into the jamal for Christmas Eve. Grandfather kicked the log now and got more fire out of it, while Hristu took charge of the roasted pig, watching to see that it kept hot without burning.

Dobry came home alone in the fresh snowstorm. The night was quiet—a hush of wonder possessed it and the locust trees were in blossom now with snow. The only one to come home covered with snow, Dobry's sheepskin cap, coat, boots of sheepskin had fleece again, all of them completely woolly with snow.

After midnight mass they broke their forty-day fast lightly. Nothing could be touched until little dried sparrows, soaked and broiled, were eaten. These were sparrows from the wheat fields that had known the growing of wheat and how the earth and its peasants worked together to produce a loaf of bread. The birds had been killed

weeks before and hung to dry under the eaves of all village houses in readiness for Christmas Eve.

"Now we eat our sparrows," Grandfather cried.

They all sat under the jamal's hood, warmed as much
by excitement as by the fire, because a sparrow eaten on
Christmas Eve is supposed to put music in the soul of a
peasant and make him feel that he has wings.

Grandfather finished his sparrow. "There—I knew it,"
he shouted. "The music is coming up in me already!"
And he began to sing before he could get the flute out
from his sash. But when the others sang, Grandfather contented himself with playing the flute while he thought,
"It's better to keep quiet and feel the spirit moving in me."

Roda and Dobry and Neda and Hristu sang the Byzantine chants heard everywhere in the village on Christmas
Eve and repeated their favorite Christmas song:

> "The Day-star of the Day-star
> And we on earth who lay
> In death-shade and in darkness
> Have found a world of Light
> For, soothly, of a virgin
> Is born the Lord of Light."

The village rose very late on Christmas morning, a
clear sharp morning with new snow on top the old. Only
Dobry got up with the tardy winter sun. He went noiselessly, crept down the rickety outside stairway, fed and
watered Sari and Pernik, fed and watered their new Beata
and the chickens, cleaned out manure and old straw from
pens and stable.

That done, Dobry stood a rough big charcoal sketch
against the poplar tree, a naked tree now except for its

snow. He massed and packed all the snow he could in a corner of the courtyard, until it piled high above his head, a small mountain of snow, immaculate, glittering with crystals of ice. Standing on a short ladder, he cut out an open stable and with great slow tenderness made the manger and the Holy Child, Mary and Joseph. Only youth could have brought the freshness Dobry brought to his Nativity, and only a primitive genius, Indian or a peasant like Dobry, could have modeled these figures with strength, assurance, sincerity—untaught in any school.

His Mary, his Joseph and Holy Child were peasants, Joseph a kindly, humorous peasant resembling Dobry's grandfather. Mary was Neda, not a beautiful Mary, but a girl strong and luminous with youth. And the child might have been any village baby looking for the abundant breasts of his peasant mother.

For the two oxen of Bethlehem, Dobry modeled his own everyday Sari and Pernik. He intended to make the ass next, because he had done it that way in the sketch. But instead he found himself modeling Neda's little goat, and wondered at the completed figure—Peter, holy now with simplicity and quietness.

Dobry told himself as an excuse for Peter's being there and nearest to the manger:

"The Child would love an animal, small like Peter, scraggly and with new horns. He would love it!"

When it was all done, Dobry looked at it and called it good. It was a dream he alone had dreamed and brought to life. The dream he had carried for months in his mind and heart had been born, and born alive.

Dobry knelt in the snow but prayed for nothing. He had already emptied his mind and heart. And now without a thought to disturb him, he felt completely one with morning and snow—at peace. Without making any noise, he went upstairs again and, tired out from his work and his feeling, threw himself on the bed in all his clothes and slept.

Grandfather went out, expecting to feed the animals and chickens, and forgot even to question how the work had been done. He took off his sheepskin cap and knelt down before the Nativity. Too forgetful of himself for prayers of asking, he knelt there, aware only of the Holy Child who had come to their home.

Roda called to him from the kitchen, "We need water. More water! Will you haul some right away?" But Grandfather never answered her. He felt that he was drinking wine.

Roda came out to hurry him, but instead of speaking, fell on her knees beside him. They stayed there together, in complete silence, forgetful of time. The Child had come to their home. And neither of them ever before had seen a Nativity like this one. The Greek Orthodox Church has paintings but no sculpture. The Child, Mary, Joseph, and the good animals blessed by the Child had been born of their snow, snow from the village sky, the water that would help create their bread and their wine.

Roda reached out her hand to touch Grandfather. She said, "You are right about Dobry. You are right. God made Dobry an artist and who am I to set my heart against it."

Tidings of the child spread abroad and not only every peasant in the village came to visit with the Holy Family, but peasants from villages miles away hitched up their buffaloes to sledges and came to pray in the snow. All day long they crowded in, and on Christmas night the court-yard was lighted by their candles and loud with their songs.

Neda came, knelt before the Nativity, and Dobry ran out to kneel beside her. Neither of them spoke, yet they said more to each other than ever before. As they came into the house Dobry whispered to Neda and his voice made her tremble.

"You are my Mary," Dobry said.

———*Monica Shannon*

Yolka (A Little Fir Tree)

THIS IS A STORY of the farthest North, the Arctic Ocean. It is a true story, and you may read about it in Russian books. What is more, you may see the proof of it in the Leningrad Arctic Museum.

In the year 1937, three well manned Russian ships went on a Polar expedition and were forced to spend the winter in the Arctic Ocean. The ships were frozen into the ice and the men were not able to sail them back to land. Thick strong heaps of ice surrounded the ships and held them fast. The temperature dipped as low as it could be measured and everybody aboard the ships knew that it wouldn't warm up for many months, for it was only the end of December. There was complete darkness all around day and night, for in the Arctic the sun doesn't appear in the sky at all during the winter months. But the men were not downhearted. Most of them had sailed in the Arctic before and they were prepared to endure the winter. Besides, all the scientists were too busy to fear or worry; they continued to make important observations of ice and wind and atmosphere; they attended to their instruments and made complicated calculations. After work there was time for rest and even for fun aboard; there were radio programs, books and games.

The writer in the crew, Konstantin Badigin, wrote long articles about life in the Arctic. Usually the articles were too long and the radio engineer, Nikolai Bekasov, kept complaining.

"I beg you, Badigin, not to write so much! Remember, I have to relay all you write by radio!" But Badigin kept writing long articles.

By the end of December the men aboard one of the ships, *The Sadko,* began to talk about the holiday preparations going on in people's homes, on land.

"I imagine," said Badigin, wistfully, "that people at home must be getting Christmas trees and decorating them with bright colored lights and toys while we are aboard ship, a thousand kilometers from the nearest forest of fir trees."

"That is nothing to worry about," answered Nikolai Bekasov, the radio engineer. "Use your imagination, Badigin. Pretend there is a fresh green fir tree aboard and you won't need to write an article about it."

"Don't make fun of me," said Badigin. "What sort of a celebration could we have without a real tree?" Then neither of them said anything more.

The next day a rumor spread aboard that there would be a tree.

"A tree?" questioned Pavel, the ship's cook. "Here, in the icy ocean?" He pushed his cook's hat back and scratched his head thoughtfully. Badigin, the writer, was specially curious.

"How could it have come to the Arctic?" he asked, trying to be practical. "Where could it have grown?"

"I don't know anything about it," answered Bekasov indifferently.

"But, who does know?" asked Yefremov, the captain's assistant. "And do you suppose Grandpa Frost will come around with presents for us, too! My, my, what surprises!"

"Yefremov, you greedy pig!" criticized Bekasov, and he shook his head and pointed his finger.

On the eve of the holiday, New Year's Eve, the doors of the ship's wardroom were flung wide open. The wardroom was the finest cabin on the ship and was used for eating and resting and meetings and entertainment. When the sailors came into the wardroom they noticed that the tables were set for a supper with unusual care, a savory odor of cooking was in the air, and the middle of the room there was—unmistakably a Christmas tree!

"Yolka!" Badigin shouted in surprise, and everyone stared in astonishment at the gorgeous sight of the green tree. It was covered with hanging sparkles, and little toys and charming frills, and it was lighted brightly with electric lights. The Yolka's branches were laden with glass cotton, light as puffs of snow and on the tip of the tree was a brilliant star. Just as it should be!

"We have a Yolka!" Yefremov shieked with delight.

"Yolka!" cried the sailors.

The tree was so beautiful, so bright, so real that it seemed a miracle. The sailors danced vigorously around it, singing their song of the Yolka that grew in the deep, green forest of Russia:

> "What merriment, what merriment,
> We're here in happy throng.
> We greet you, Yolka, gleefully
> With season's gayest song."

Pavel, the cook, stood by the table with a proud grin, noticing how everyone sniffed and looked expectantly. Badigin had written in his latest article that the cook had worked several days on the preparation of the holiday supper. And what a supper it was! There were plenty of meat and fish dishes, and a platter of baked goodies was placed attractively in the middle of the table. The ship's dogs, Jerry and Icicle, sniffed excitedly all during the meal. The dogs had always had enough to eat, but on that New Year's Eve, they were simply stuffed.

After supper, the dogs relaxed in the warm wardroom and sprawled under the table and dosed peacefully. Suddenly both of them jumped, bristled up, and barking loudly, dashed toward the door. Every one in the cabin looked instantly toward the door. . . . And there, smiling most genially, was Grandpa Frost himself. He walked slowly into the cabin, swinging heavily from side to side. He had a jolly red nose, and a long white beard. He was dressed properly in a long fur coat, and a big fat bag was slung across his shoulders. A real, honest to goodness Grandpa Frost such as can be seen in the pictures.

"Look at that!" cried Yefremov, pointing his finger at the large bag.

Grandpa Frost walked over calmly to the little Yolka and said, in a peculiarly familiar voice:

"Please, gentlemen, accept my gifts." He bowed cere-
moniously and dug into his bag. Out came, first of all, an
enormous pencil, the size of a flute. "This is for you, Con-
stantin Badigin, so that you can write *longer* articles for
the papers." There was unmistakable sarcasm in the word
longer, and everyone laughed.

Other presents followed. Yefremov, to his great delight,
received the biggest package of all. When he untied the
ribbon and unwrapped the newspaper, he found a box.
Inside the box was another package wrapped in newspaper
and tied with ribbon. When he untied and unwrapped that,
he found another box. Everyone crowded around to see
what was in *that* box. There was a third smaller package,
and inside that a third, smaller box. Then came a fourth
and a fifth box! Everyone roared with laughter as Yefremov continued unwrapping one box after another, each
one smaller than the one before, of course. Finally, in
the tenth box there was the present. It was a very tiny baby
doll. Yefremov held it in his big strong hands, and passed
it around to all of his laughing comrades.

Pavel, the cook, received half a dozen pairs of dark
glasses which protect the eyes from the blinding sparkle
of snow when the sun shines. They were, of course, useless
in the Arctic winter when there was no sun at all!

Fourteen times Grandpa Frost dipped his hand into the
bag full of presents. When he put his hand in for the
fifteenth time, he announced curiously, "And this is for
me!" There was nothing there! Then he pulled off his
beard, took off his fur coat, yanked off his red nose that
had been pasted onto his face and became transformed
into the radio engineer Nikolai Bekasov.

"So you are Grandpa Frost! Bekasov, you rascal!"

shouted Badigin. They shook hands vigorously, in a true Russian fashion, and Badigin bumped into the Yolka. As he touched the tree, somehow it didn't feel like a fir tree. "Look, comrades!" he shouted, inspecting the tree. "Look where our Yolka came from!" Everybody looked and touched the little green Yolka and gasped and laughed merrily at the discovery. For the beautiful Yolka proved to be home-made, not forest grown.

Nikolai Bekasov, with the help of several sailors, had thought up the trick of taking a stick and attaching to it twigs from the deck broom. This make-believe tree was colored and covered and became the home-made Yolka, perfectly fitting for the New Year's celebration in the Arctic.

To this day, the home-made broom-twig Yolka is in the Leningrad Arctic Museum, and all the men who had enjoyed it aboard a ship are celebrating the season with a beautiful Yolka, a lovely green fir tree from the deep forests of Russia.

——*Marguerita Rudolph*

Carol of the Russian Children

Snow-bound mountains,
Snow-bound valleys,
Snow-bound plateaus, clad in white.
Fur-robed moujiks, fur-robed nobles,
Fur-robed children, see the light.

Shaggy pony, shaggy oxen,
Gentle shepherds wait the light;
Little Jesu, little mother,
Good St. Joseph, come this night.
Light! Light! Light!

——*Author unknown*

In Clean Hay

IN A LITTLE VILLAGE on the outskirts of the Polish city of Krakow there stands a happy farmhouse whose owner is Pan Jan. In the early spring the fields about the house are dark and rich, awaiting the planting of seed; and in the summer they are green with ripened grain. In the fall they turn to russet brown; and in the winter they lie deep beneath the shining snow. From earliest morning until sundown the house is astir with action, but at sundown everything ceases and peace descends, for did the Lord not ordain all work should cease with the sun? Then the lamp is lighted in the large room and the newspaper which has come from Krakow will be read to all the family by the father or the eldest boy, Antek. The others sit about and listen. Antek is fifteen and goes every day to the high school in the city; it is a walk of about three miles, but the road is good and there is often company on the way.

Antek reads from the gazette: "To-morrow is the day before Christmas and there will be many visitors who come to the city to attend services at night in the churches. The Christmas trees will be on sale in the Rynek (market place) and the booths full of candy and toys will be opened directly after dark. In the homes, the children will await the sight of the first star: when the first star shines, then an angel will come and knock at the door, and rejoicing at the birth of Christ will begin. This year there will be a special treat for Krakow people, for a very famous performer will give his puppet play, the Szopka Krakowska, at the Falcon Hall on Grodska Street. With him will be his wife, who will sing the hymns."

Antek put down the paper. "Our puppet show is all made."

The father: "Don't stay out too late."

Antek answered quickly: "No, little father, we won't. We will give our show several times between five and seven o'clock and then we will start on the road home."

In one corner of the little farmhouse stood a small, wooden two-towered church in miniature; between the towers at the base, large doors stood wide open, revealing a stage. And on this stage were piled a number of little wooden figures, like dolls, dressed in various jaunty colors, and in the background was a figure of a woman with a baby in her arms. This was a stage in miniature—a Szopka Krakowska with its little wooden puppets. When set up up for the entertainment of lookers-on, Antek would crawl beneath it and operate the puppets from little sticks that went through a slot in the floor. This slot extended the whole length of the stage, so that a puppet could be brought upon the scene from one side, made to perform, and then be taken away on the farther side. During the performance of a puppet play the figures moved in constant succession across this stage.

The mother entered from the stove room with a huge pot of steaming soup and poured it out into wooden bowls before each of the children.

"Well, to-morrow will be Christmas Eve," she said.

"And make a lot of money." This was from Stefan, the second in age. He was a more practical boy than his brother, although younger—yet he had less of the vivid imagination which made Antek the better showman of the puppet show.

The mother sighed. "I wish we could give it to you; but what we have is being laid by against the days when you go up to the university. How much did you make last year?"

"We'll make a hundred this year," said Stefan.

"And what will you do with it?" asked the mother.

A clamor went up. Antek was saying something about a book, Stefan about a chest of tools, and Anusia, the "Baby" of ten years, said something that sounded like "Shoes." Christopher, who played all the songs for the Szopka on his violin, tried to make known his want for new strings and a bow. However, the whole pandemonium was such that anyone might see that at least something was wanted rather eagerly: it was true, as the mother had said, that the scanty profits from the farm were going into the children's educations: Antek for the university, Stefan for the school of commerce and trade, Christopher

for the academy of music, and Anusia—for—well, that
would come later. The child had a clear and appealing
voice, and might become a great singer if placed with the
proper teachers. Who knows?

Therefore this chance of making a little money on the
night before Christmas meant a great deal to them all.
The boys, working with the father, had built the little
theater themselves. It stood upon little folding legs which
Stefan had devised. The mother had dressed the dolls,
and on the night before Christmas it was all in readiness
to carry to Krakow. Now, since the very earliest days of
the city, boys have gone about in Krakow giving this
show on Christmas Eve, most of them poor or needy boys
to whom the gift of money was a veritable godsend. And
on Christmas Eve there descends over the earth, each year,
that spirit of gladness and kindness that makes people
eager and anxious to relieve suffering and soften the hard
ways of life with the cheer that the Christ Child brought
to men.

The day before Christmas dawned bright. It was crisp
but not so cold as usual. There was not a cloud in the
sky, and the children knew that they could not have
selected a better day for their puppet show. At about one
o'clock in the afternoon they started for Krakow. Antek
walked in front with the Szopka strapped to his shoulders.
Stefan, carrying the sticks on which the Szopka was to
rest, walked by his side. Christopher on the left side,
carrying his violin and bow in a case in one hand, had
extended the other hand to Anusia, who walked just beyond. A happy company it was, and all along the way
people greeted them and shouted out "Wesolych Swait
(Merry Christmas)." or else "Niech bendzie pochwalony

Jesus Christ." (May Jesus Christ be praised.) As they neared the city the sun was sinking, for they had walked slowly and, too, the sun sinks early in the Christmas season. Lights were coming on everywhere, and as they stood at the Florain Gate, Anusia turning about screamed with delight and pointed at the sky.

For there, hanging like a little candle, was the first star. The Christmas season had begun.

In the market place they selected a corner by one path and mounted the puppet theater on its legs. "It was here that we stood last year," said Antek.

Candles were lighted before the little theater; a crowd gathered. Then Anusia stepped out before the people, and bravely sang a little carol, while Christopher played on the violin. The crowd increased:

"Oh, what a crowd!" cried Stefan, rubbing his hands. "Here at least for the first performance is a good twenty-five Zlotys." His words were correct. The first performance netted exactly that amount. It was a splendid performance too: Anusia sang the carols beautifully, Antek made the puppets dance as if they were alive, and everybody reached for handkerchiefs when King Herod ordered that all the babies in the Kingdom should be put to death.

They had begun again when suddenly there came a rude end to their performance, and to all their hopes.

A dignitary wearing a huge star stepped into the circle before the little theater and ordered the play to be stopped.

"We can't!" shrieked Stefan, who was reading the lines for the puppets. "Don't bother us. The show must go on."

The dignitary grinned. "Where is your license?" he asked.

"License?" Antek crept out from beneath the theater where he was operating the puppets and faced the officer.

"Yes. Don't you know that you must buy a license to give public performances in this city?"

"No. It was not so last year."

"But it is so this year. It is a new ordinance that no shows may be given on the streets without a license."

"How much is the license?" asked Antek.

"One hundred Zlotys," said the man.

"But I haven't got one hundred Zlotys!" groaned Antek.

"Then you must move along or I will report you to the police." He motioned to a police officer on the corner.

"Come quick," ordered Antek, snatching up the theater to his back. "Take the stool Stefan, and you, Anusia, hang on to Christopher."

They emerged in a quiet place behind the Cloth Hall to take counsel.

"We can't do anything. We've got to go home," Antek announced. Every face fell. Anusia began to cry. "It can't be helped. We must obey the law and we haven't one hundred Zlotys in the world."

"Let's give the show in some private street," suggested Stefan.

"Can't be done. We'd be arrested."

They marched out into the street. Two men engaged in a spirited conversation almost ran them down.

"Look out there," said one, sidestepping the Szopka. "The street doesn't belong to you boys."

"No, but we have our rights," answered Antek.

"That you have," answered the second man suddenly striking Antek in friendly fashion upon the back. "A Szopka, as I live!"

"A Szopka—" the second man fell back in amazement.

"Yes, and a good one," said the first man examining the show quickly. "Here is an answer to our prayers sent from Heaven. Do you people operate the Szopka?"

"We do," answered Antek wonderingly.

"Do you want an engagement?"

"Yes!" shouted Antek, Stefan and Christopher at the tops of their voices.

"Then come with us. You see, we were to have had a very famous Szopka with us to-night—Pan Kowalski and his wife were to entertain us. The crowd is all there— has been for half an hour—waiting for the show to begin. And there is no Pan Kowalski. We have looked up and down the town; we have hunted all through the villages, we have inquired everywhere that he might have been, and yet we cannot find him. We must have the show or send the people home."

"How much do we get?" asked Stefan, characteristically, for he had recovered from his astonishment at this quick turn of affairs.

"We will take a collection. We can at least guarantee you one hundred Zlotys. You will probably make much more than that."

As they spoke the two men hustled the children along Grodska Street and stopped in front of a building on which there was a coat of arms bearing the figure of a falcon.

"In here," said one of the men.

"Why this is the Falcon Hall we read of in the newspaper," said Stefan. "This is the best place in Krakow in which to give the Szopka. Antek, do you realize"—he turned to his brother, "that we will make lots of money out of this?"

"We must give a good performance first," admonished Antek.

One of the men made a speech to the people, while the children prepared the show. He was sorry, he said, that Pan Kowalski had not been able to come. But in his place there had come a very fine Szopka operated by young men who were quite experienced—at this the crowd laughed, for the youth of the performers was quite evident. "It is Christmas Eve," the man went on. "And it is not the time to show any displeasure. We have come here to see acted the old story of the wonderful evening so many centuries ago when Christ was born to earth to bring peace and goodwill to all men."

It was a Christmas crowd at that, and if it felt any ill will at this substitution on the program, it did not show it. The lamp in front of the stage was lighted. Antek stepped out in front and played on his little bugle the Heynal, or little trumpet song that the trumpeter in the tower of the church of Our Lady had played every hour of the day and night since Christianity in Krakow began. Then lights appeared in the two towers, and Christopher and Anusia stepped out to play and sing the old hymn, "Amid the Silence." The curtains were swept back by Stefan, and there on the stage were two shepherds sleeping. Red fire is burned, an angel descends, and again Christopher and Anusia step forward. This time the song is "Gloria in Excelsis," the song sung by the angels when Christ was born. The curtain is closed. It opens again on Bethlehem, whither the shepherds have come to greet the Christ Child, who lies there with the Mother, asleep on the clean hay. From the back of the manger a sheep and a cow look over the wall.

Then the scene changes. We are now in the court of Herod, the King, and Three Kings come in from the east to ask their way to the new-born King; Herod cannot tell them and so they go out again and follow a star that is gleaming in the heavens; here Stefan lifts into the air a great gold star which shines with brilliance when the light falls upon it. They come to the Christ Child and they too worship. Then the shepherds dance, and the soldiers sing and the violin makes merry music for all the company. It is truly a splendid sight; the children shout, the babies crow, and the men and women clap their hands in applause.

O thou cruel Herod! For now he commands his Headman to send out the soldiers and destroy the Christ Child; but because they do not know who the Christ Child is, they must destroy every child in the Kingdom. Cruel King Herod, for this thou shalt pay—for the floor of the stage opens and the Devil dances out; how the children scream as he cuts off Herod's head, and the head goes rolling out of the little theater and onto the floor. Then there comes more dancing and singing; little Anusia sings like an angel—the men and women take her up and the children kiss her and stroke her hands.

And when the collection is taken the bowl is heaped high with paper and silver and copper. There are at least five hundred Zlotys upon the plate (about fifty dollars), the best day's work that any Szopka has ever done in Krakow. The crowd leaves slowly; the men come and take their leave of the children; the show is packed up, and the four, now beaming with happiness and delight, take again the road for the village three miles away. It is a lovely night, not over cold, but just comfortably cold, and though there is no moon, the stars are as bright as the little pine points of light in the Szopka walls. As they pass the Church of Our Lady they hear the trumpet playing the Heynal, and it makes them feel suddenly that over all the world has come this happiness at the birth of Christ.

Two hours later, on the road still, they put into the home of neighbor Kolesza for a rest. He meets them at the door with a Christmas greeting and then tells them to come to the stable for there they will find a surprise.

"I had no room for them in the house," he said. "The hay in the stable is much warmer than my floor and I have a stove here where I have heat for the animals in winter. Come and you shall see."

They entered the stable. He flashed his lantern high above his head—they looked—they drew their breaths— and then with one accord fell upon their knees.

For there in the manger was a young woman. She had been sleeping but was now awake; and in her arms, nestled close to her body, was a little baby, wrapped in a blue coat.

"It is the Christ Child," whispered Stefan. "See, there is the cow and the sheep looking over the back of the manger; and there is the place where the Wise Men knelt." He pointed—indeed a dark figure arose there and looked about; it was a man, and he put his fingers to his lips lest they should talk and disturb the mother and child.

"It is Pan Kowalski the puppet-show man," said Pan Kolesza in an undertone. "He was on his way to Krakow to-night to give a performance in the hall of the Falcons.

He and his wife stopped here; and while they were here this child was born."

The children looked at one another strangely. Then they looked at Pan Kowalski, and then at the mother and the child.

"They have no money," went on Pan Kolesza; "they were to have received much money for their performance in Krakow to-night, but they were not able to go, and therefore they lose it. I do not know what they will do when they leave here, though the good God knows I will let them stay as long as they like. They have only this show which they give at Christmas; it is not given at any other time of the year."

"And it was on this night that Christ was born. . . ." said Antek. "Stefan . . ." he added after a long pause.

"I know what you are going to say," retorted Stefan. They went out into the air again, not even taking leave of either of the men, so engrossed were they in their own thoughts.

"No," said Stefan. "Let me."

Antek squeezed something into his hand. Stefan ran back to the stable and entered. Pan Kowalski had sunk into a stupor again and heeded nothing; Stefan crept up to the manger and listened to the deep breathing of the mother. Then he slipped his hand over the edge of the manger and dropped all the silver and notes that had been collected in Krakow; then he fell upon his knees for a moment and said a little prayer. But as he staggered after his companions down the long dark road, something of the most infinite happiness seized upon his heart, and when he reached Antek he was sobbing like a baby. Whereupon Antek fell to sobbing likewise, and out there

upon the Krakow road Christ was born again in the hearts
of four happy children.

——*Eric P. Kelly*

Before the Paling of the Stars

Before the paling of the stars,
   Before the winter morn,
Before the earliest cock-crow
   Jesus Christ was born:
Born in a stable,
   Cradled in a manger,
In the world His hands had made
   Born a stranger.

Priest and King lay fast asleep
   In Jerusalem,
Young and old lay fast asleep
   In crowded Bethlehem:
Saint and Angel, ox and ass,
   Kept a watch together,
Before the Christmas daybreak
   In the winter weather.

Jesus on his mother's breast
   In the stable cold,
Spotless Lamb of God was He
   Shepherd of the fold:
Let us kneel with Mary Maid,
   With Joseph bent and hoary,
With Saint and Angel, ox and ass,
   To hail the King of Glory.
      ——*Christina G. Rossetti*

"Before the Paling of the Stars" is from the *Poetical Works of Christina Rossetti;* reprinted by permission of The Macmillan Company.

"KINDLE THE TAPER LIKE THE
STEADFAST STAR"

——*Emma Lazarus*

What Is Hanukkah? (The Festival of Lights)

Commencing with the twenty-fifth day of the month Kislev, there are eight days upon which there shall be neither mourning nor fasting. For albeit the Greeks entered the Temple and defiled the oil, it was when the might of the Hasmonean (Maccabean) overcame and vanquished them, that, upon search, a single cruse of oil sealed by the High Priest was found. In it was oil enough for the needs of a solitary day.

Then it was that the miracle was wrought.

The oil in the cruse burned eight days.

——*Babylonian Talmud C.E. 500*

For Hanukkah

Father lighted candles for me;
　Like a torch the *Shamash* shone.
In whose honor, for whose glory?
　For Hanukkah alone.

Teacher bought a big top for me,
　Solid lead, the finest known.
In whose honor, for whose glory?
　For Hanukkah alone.

Mother made a pancake for me,
　Hot and sweet and sugar-strewn.
In whose honor, for whose glory?
　For Hanukkah alone.

Uncle had a present for me,
　An old penny for my own.
In whose honor, for whose glory?
　For Hanukkah alone.
　　　　　　——*H. N. Bialek*

"For Hanukkah" by H. N. Bialek, is from *Far Over the Sea;* copyright, 1939, by the Union of American Hebrew Congregations; reprinted by permission.

Bobby's Best Hanukkah

IT WAS THANKSGIVING DAY and the day of the
big football game. This was set for a quarter of nine to
give the boys time to get back home and dressed for the
Union Thanksgiving service. Bobby was lucky, for the
service was to be around the corner from his house at
the First Methodist Church.

When Bobby woke up and looked out of the window
it wasn't dark as he had expected. Then he knew what
had happened. During the night the first snow of the
season had fallen and the whole street was covered with
its bright whiteness. He didn't like the snow so well
because it wouldn't make it any easier to play football.
As it grew lighter, though, he saw that the snow wasn't
deep and he said to himself, "I guess we can make it all
right today. For once our first string line is healthy and

we have a good chance of coming out on top. We are counting on this game."

Bobby's Mom and Dad, Mr. and Mrs. Frankfurter, had planned to sleep later than usual Thanksgiving morning so Bobby stayed in bed as long as he could. How the bed springs creaked and the floor squeaked when he crept out of bed and shut his window! But he got into his football outfit before his Dad stuck his head in the door.

"Hello, Son," he said. "I see you are all set for the big game."

"I'm so set I can feel the pigskin in my arms," Bobby answered.

"Good," said Dad. "I'll get the car out of the garage after breakfast and drive you over to the school yard. I'll watch the first half of the game, then I have to get a package at the drug store and come home to give mother a hand with the table. The Fullers and the Goodmans are having dinner with us today."

Mother called Bobby to breakfast and although he had orange juice and milk and cereal he was too excited to know what he was eating. All he could think of was today's game and the last one of the season.

Outside the air was fresh and cold, just right for football. The cleats on his shoes made marks in the snow and Bobby drew pictures with them while Dad backed the car out of the garage. He drew a snow picture of three Pilgrims, a goal post, and a turkey gobbler. Then Dad pulled up and off they went to the school yard.

All the boys, Bobby, Tommy, Dan and the whole team were on time and they ran through their signals before Coach Sheffing blew his whistle. The boys played the best game they had ever played. The Eighth Grade team were good, too, and the score was 6 to 6 at the end of the third quarter. Then, when the fourth quarter was almost over, it was Tommy's forty-six-yard run for a touchdown that broke the tie and Bobbie's team had won the game. The boys hugged each other in glee and wanted to linger in the school yard to talk things over but they hurried home and managed to come to the services early enough so that they could visit together on the church steps about the game.

"More later," said Bobby, for Tommy and Danny were coming to his house for dinner. The Goodmans always had Thanksgiving dinner at Bobby's and this year, because Mr. Fuller had to be away, Mrs. Fuller and Tommy had been invited also. Then, together the boys went into the service. It had been Rabbi Goodman's turn to preach the Thanksgiving sermon this year and Bobby's father stood with him as he shook hands at the door with all of the people who had come to church that morning. The three boys' mothers and Bobby's sister, Judy, hurried home to get dinner ready. Bobby and Dan followed after them while Tommy ran home to get the cranberry jelly his mother had made for the dinner.

Suddenly the boys were startled by the sound of screeching automobile brakes and then they heard their fathers calling. They ran back to the corner and there, in the street, they saw Tommy lying, in front of a waiting machine.

"Run quick, Danny," said Mr. Frankfurter, "and get Dr. Levy. I saw him drive up to his house and I know he is home. And you, Bob, tell mother to get the downstairs bedroom ready and put some water on to boil."

Then Rabbi Goodman, Dr. Levy, the driver of the

automobile and Bobby's father used the back seat of the car for a stretcher and brought Tommy into the house. Bobby's father motioned to the boys with his head and they knew they were to wait outside. This was very hard on Bobby because Tommy had always been his best friend. They had started school together in the First Grade and, after school, where either one was, the other wasn't far away. It isn't easy to stay outside and wait to hear what has happened to your best friend.

The boys couldn't stand still so they walked back to the corner and there they could see by the tracks that Tommy had run across the street diagonally, in the middle of the block. "Tommy couldn't have heard the car coming because of the snow," said Dan.

"No," said Bobby, "and see where the car skidded when the driver put on his brakes "

Then Bobby noticed a red puddle close to the curbing and grabbed Dan's arm to hold himself steady before he realized the puddle wasn't what he thought it was but, instead, it was cranberry jelly spilled in the snow. Up against the tree trunk there he noticed something bright and shiny. It was the copper bowl Mrs. Fuller always used to mold the jelly only now it was bent flat and torn. Dan picked it up and as they went back threw it down in Bobby's yard. Bobby looked at it and it had been torn in so many places that it made him think of the Menorah, Hanukkah's eight-branched candlestick. For a moment he forgot about Tommy and thought only of Hanukkah and the fun ahead. He was glad that Hanukkah came early this year; it wouldn't be so hard to say goodbye to the football season, with that to look forward to.

Then a lump came in Bobby's throat and even Dan was

quiet for once. All about it seemed terribly still. Then Bobby saw the pictures he had made in the snow that morning, only one Pilgrim, the turkey and a picture he had only started to make were left. As the boys stood there, Bobby finished the picture. With the toe of his shoe he drew an outline of an eight-branched candlestick!

At last the door opened. It was Rabbi Goodman who came out. "It is too early to know," he said. "Dr. Levy thinks it is serious and it will take several days before Tommy is out of danger."

"Will he have to go to the hospital?" asked Bobby.

"No," said Rabbi Goodman. "Your father and mother have asked if he can stay here and the doctor thinks this will be a good plan. They will bring a portable X-ray unit here and Tommy will have every care he would have in the hospital."

Bobby felt better. He could have his best friend in his house and maybe there would be things he could do to help.

"It is three o'clock," the Rabbi said. "You boys should be hungry. You had a good work-out this morning."

Dan said he wasn't hungry and Bobby did, too. Then Bobby knew he had an empty feeling in his stomach and was glad when Dan's father added that he was going to the kitchen where Dr. Levy and Bobby's father were visiting while Judy, his sister, stood listening.

"Come on, Judy," said her father, "let's make some sandwiches." So the five of them, Bobby and his father, Rabbi Goodman, Judy and Dan ate some of the Thanksgiving dinner Bobby's mother had prepared so carefully.

"There is not much I can tell you about Tommy now," said Dr. Levy. "The X-rays will tell if he has a concussion and if that's it, we won't know much for several days. It may even be a week or more."

"Does it hurt much?" asked Bobby.

"No, Robert, it doesn't hurt at all," answered Dr. Levy. "He's unconscious and feels no pain whatever."

"When will he wake up?" Danny asked.

"Whether he wakes up or not, Daniel, is all in God's hands. But Thomas has always been a fine, healthy fellow. Maybe he will have the strength to get well." Then Dr. Levy straightened himself up and smiled at the boys and said, "We are all going to pull together to bring him through this."

Bobby's mother came to the door, "The X-ray people are here," she announced. And Dr. Levy was right. Tommy did have a concussion.

Thanksgiving day dragged for Bobby and when bedtime came, tired as he was, he couldn't go to sleep. The house seemed like a hospital and that was what it was. The boys had helped Mr. Frankfurter move the living room furniture around to make room for a cot they had brought up from the basement for Tommy's mother to sleep on. Rabbi and Mrs. Goodman went to the Fuller's house to get some clothes for her. Judy helped mother bring sheets and pillow cases and towels down stairs so they would be handy for the nurse to use and there were all kinds of errands to do and phone calls to be made. Then, too, people came to the back door to ask about Tommy and to offer their help. After the first rush was over it was just as the doctor said, there wasn't much anyone could do but wait for Tommy to wake up and Bobby knew that might not happen.

Before the Goodmans left for home, everybody gathered

in the kitchen. Even Mrs. Fuller came in. She was very quiet and she looked older and tired. Rabbi Goodman said a prayer for Tommy and although this made Bobby want to cry, he felt better. Then everybody said goodnight and Dr. Levy promised to come over early in the morning.

Bobby's mother went upstairs with him and tucked him in his bed and said, "Go to sleep, son." But that wasn't easy. Bobby kept thinking about all the things that had happened. The morning had been such fun. Suddenly Bobby sat straight up in bed. "Hanukkah is only eight days off," he thought, "that is always the happiest day of the year for me. Eight days. . . . That is just a little more than a week. By that time Dr. Levy said we will know about Tommy. If he could live to Hanukkah, Tommy will be all right."

Then, Bobby thought on. Why Tommy is like the cruse of oil that had been found half hidden in the ruins of Jerusalem, more than two thousand years ago. Judas Maccabeus had been sure there was only oil enough left to keep the lamp burning on the altar one single day. But the lamp burned on, day after day, and was still aglow when the new oil was brought on the eighth day. Dr. Levy had said that Tommy might not have strength to live on until the injury to his brain had healed, but Bobby thought in his heart, that Tommy would stay alive and get well and that this Hanukkah would be the happiest he had ever had.

Friday morning, Dr. Levy came and said, "No change!"
Saturday and Sunday he said, "Tommy is holding his own." And Monday, "Tommy is a shade better."
Tuesday, Dr. Levy came as Bobby was starting for

school. "Tommy's not out of danger but his condition is encouraging," he announced. Bobby could hardly keep from grinning. "The old cruse is going strong," he thought. By Wednesday even the doctor was grinning and when Bobby came home from school at noon his mother met him at the front door. "Tommy's awake," she said. "He's still very weak but he's conscious." "Of course he's weak," thought Bobby, "I guess even the light in the Temple wasn't so bright the seventh day." But still he kept what he had been thinking to himself.

The next morning Bobby's mother was sitting on the side of his bed. "Bobby," she said, "I really believe Tommy is out of danger." Bobby gave her a great big hug and was about to let out a shriek of "Yippee," but she grabbed him and held her hand over his mouth.

"Steady there, not so fast," she warned. "Rome wasn't built in a day, you know."

"Neither was the Temple rebuilt that fast," Bobby said.

"What ever are you talking about," asked Mrs. Frankfurter.

But Bobby changed the subject. "Mom," he said, "do you think maybe I could light the first Hanukkah candle, tonight in Tom's room, so he could see it?"

"I'll ask Dr. Levy when he comes," she answered. Then, she added, "I've been too busy to make the usual preparations for Hanukkah. I hope you won't be too disappointed."

"I'd much rather wait with the real fun until Tommy is better. After all, there are eight days of Hanukkah, and maybe Tom will be well before it is over. Then we could celebrate all of it together."

Dr. Levy came early that day and it was just as Bobby's

mother had predicted. "Tommy is going to get well," he said. "And," he added, "Bobby can go into his room for just a moment at dusk and light the first of the Hanukkah lights." Bobby rode to school in Dr. Levy's car and asked if Tommy couldn't stay in his house for the eight days of Hanukkah and Dr. Levy answered that this would be a good plan. Then, he added, "Tommy has some fun coming to him!"

That night Mrs. Frankfurter had the beautiful copper candlestick with the lions decorating it freshly polished. It had been her father's and she had lighted her own Hanukkah candles in it when she was a little girl. Bobby liked mother's candlestick but he also liked his own, the one his Aunt Ann had sent him last year.

Then, as it was beginning to get dark, the nurse called him and Bobby went into Tommy's room with the two Menorahs. He took the golden candles they had given him in Sunday School—two boxes this year for he had asked for a box for Tommy who was going to be a visitor all through the Hanukkah celebration.

Tommy smiled up at Bobby from his pillow. "Hi," he said.

"Hi, there, yourself," Bobby answered. Then he imitated the voice of their patrol captain at school, "Next time, you'll cross the street at the corner."

Both boys laughed.

"I can't stay long this time," said Bobby, "but we're going to have some fun from now on. Tonight's the first night of Hanukkah, and I am going to light the first Hanukkah candle, now, and leave one in the window for you to watch. Which one shall it be?"

Tommy pointed to Bobby's mother's, the one with the

standing lions and Bobby repeated the Hanukkah blessing:

"Praised be Thou, O Lord our God, Ruler of the World, who hast sanctified us by Thy commandments and bidden us kindle the Hanukkah lights. Praised be Thou, O Lord our God, Ruler of the World, who didst wondrous things for our fathers at this season in those days. Praised be Thou, O Lord our God, Ruler of the World, who hast granted us life, sustained us and permitted us to celebrate this joyous festival."

Then lighting the two *Shamus* candles, Bobby gave Tommy one, "You do what I do," he said and they each lighted the candle at the left of the Menorahs. Bobby put the copper one on the table by the window, picked up the other one and waved goodnight as he went out of the room.

Everyday Tommy got stronger, and every evening Bobby was allowed to stay in his room a little longer. The second night Tommy wanted to light the new Menorah and after they had each lighted two candles Bobby surprised him by turning on the music box inside it and they both listened to the tune of Rock of Ages, the Hanukkah song. Tommy had never heard it before. Next day, Tommy sat up a little bit and Bobby's mother and Mrs. Fuller fixed their suppers on a table in his room. There were packages on the table, two of them, exactly alike, their first Hanukkah gifts. When the boys opened them, there were two new football uniforms, a size too large, so they would fit next year.

Bobby put the Menorahs on each window and watched their candles burn down. Some of the tallow spilled over the sides and formed little golden figures and Bobby wondered if the idols the Syrians worshipped hadn't looked like that. He wanted to talk about it, but Tommy's mother came in to put him to bed.

"Would you like to read to Tommy when you come home from school tomorrow?" his mother asked.

So the next day Bobby found the Hanukkah story in one of his Sunday School books and read the chapter that told how Judas Maccabeus and his little band of warriors had defeated the mighty armies of the mad Syrian ruler, Antiochus. The Syrians had tried by every means to force their Jewish subjects to give up their own religion. They had even tried to ruin the beautiful Temple, and had put their own idols on the very altar. But finally the mad Antiochus, Emperor of the Syrians, was driven out of Jerusalem by the Maccabees, who were few in number but strong in faith.

"What happened after the Syrians were defeated?" Tommy wanted to know.

"The very first thing the Jews did was to clean up the Temple, and rededicate it to the worship of the one God of the universe," Bobby laughed as he added, "But they would have had an awful time if it hadn't been for you."

"What are you talking about?" said Tommy. "And who's the sick one now, you or I?"

When Bobby could stop laughing, he told Tommy the story of the cruse of oil that kept the eternal light burning on the altar for eight days and how he had remembered it the night Tommy was so sick, exactly eight days before Hanukkah and was sure Tommy would last out the eight days, too. Bobby called Tommy, "Old Cruse," and Tommy called Bobby, "Maccabee," and Bobby said, "Swell, that means the 'hammer' because Judas was so strong and brave.

"You know," Bobby went on, "there is a sort of connection between Thanksgiving and Hanukkah. The Jews could have lived on comfortably and easily if they had been willing to give up their religion. But they were like the Pilgrims. They both went through hardships and made great sacrifices so that they could worship their God in the way they thought right." And so the boys talked about the Pilgrims and the Maccabees until it was time to light the candles again.

The days passed quickly. Every night the boys played with the games they received and once in a while their parents joined in, telling riddles and singing songs. Then Friday came, and Tommy's last day. When Bobby came home from school, his mother shooed him into Tommy's room and told him to stay there. Tommy had to stay in bed and rest because this was the last night of Hanukkah but his best suit was laid out for him to wear when he got up.

Finally, when Bobby's dad opened the door, there was a loud yell; "S-U-R-P-R-I-S-E, S-u-r-p-r-i-s-e!" And there were all the boys on the football team and Coach Sheffing, too. Bobby's mother and dad had planned a wonderful party for the last night of Hanukkah. The living room was decorated; Coach Sheffing stood at one end and made a speech telling how glad the team was that Tommy was well again and would be back to school soon—ready for the basket ball season. Then Bobby's mother asked everyone to go into the dining room for supper. All the Menorahs were placed there ready to light—five of them, for Danny and Bill and Joe had brought theirs along.

Then Bobby recited the Hanukkah blessing and the boys lighted the candles, every single one of them, forty-five, counting the Shamuses. Then the electric lights were turned off and the Hanukkah lights made the room beautifully bright. Bobby's mother sat down at the piano and all the boys who knew it sang:

> "Rock of ages, let our song
> Praise Thy saving power."

The song sounded weak at first but by the time its three verses had been sung through, all the boys came out strong on the last lines:

> "Ours the message cheering
> That the time is nearing
> Which shall see
> All men free,
> Tyrants disappearing!"

It was a wonderful evening for everybody. It wasn't just the good things they had to eat, or their Hanukkah gifts, or the games they played. It was all of them put together, and having Tommy well again. But the whole week had been wonderful. When a boy's pal is around to share things with him, everything is more fun, and Hanukkah, the happiest week of the year, had been the happiest week in Bobby's life. And the fun wasn't over yet, for the day after Hanukkah, when Tommy went home at last, Bobby's mother promised him that he could accept Tommy's invitation and spend the Christmas holidays at his house.

——*Ruth Atlas Binstock*

Dreidel Song

Twirl about, dance about,
Spin, spin, spin!
Turn, Dreidel, turn—
Time to begin!

Soon it is Hanukkah—
Fast Dreidel, fast!
For you will lie still
When Hanukkah's past.
———*Efraim Rosenzweig*

The Hanukkah top is sometimes called a *Dreidel,* sometimes a *Trendel.*

K'tonton Arrives

ONCE UPON A TIME there lived a husband and a wife. They had everything in the world to make them happy, or almost everything; a good snug house, clothes to keep them warm, white bread, wine, and fish for Friday night and a "kugel" every Sabbath. Only one thing was missing and that was a child.

"Ah," the woman would sigh, "if only I could have a child! I shouldn't mind if he were no bigger than a thumb."

One day—it was *Succoth,* the Feast of the Tabernacles —she was praying in the Synagogue, when she happened to look down. There at her side stood a little old woman with deep, kind eyes peering up at her from under a shawl!

"K'tonton Arrives" is from *Adventures of K'tonton,* by Sadie Rose Weilerstein; copyright, 1935, by The Women's League of the United Synagogue of America. The inclusion of this story does not indicate the endorsement by the Women's League of joint Christmas-Hanukah celebrations.

"Why do you look so sad," asked the old woman, "and why do you pray so earnestly?"

"I am sad," answered the wife, "because I have no child. Ah! that I might have a child! I shouldn't mind if he were no bigger than a thumb."

"In that case," said the little old woman, "I shall tell you what to do! Has your husband an *ethrog?*"

"Indeed he has," said the wife, "and *ethrog,* a *mehuder.*" (That means that it was a very fine *ethrog,* a perfect, sweet-smelling one, a citron that had come all the way from Palestine.)

"Then," said the old woman, "on the last day of *Succoth* you must take the *ethrog* and bite off the end, and you shall have your wish."

The wife thanked the little old woman kindly. When the last day of *Succoth* came, she bit off the end of the *ethrog* just as she had been told. Sure enough, before the year had passed a little boy was born to her. It was a dear little boy baby, with black eyes and hair, dimples in his knees, and thumbs just right for sucking. There was only one thing queer about him. He was exactly the size of a thumb, not one bit smaller or larger.

The wife laughed when she saw him. I don't know whether she laughed because she was so glad, or because it seemed so funny to have a baby as big as a thumb. Whichever it was, the husband said, "We shall call him Isaac, because Isaac means laughter." Then because they were so thankful to God for sending him, they gave the baby a second name, Samuel. But, of course, you couldn't call so wee a little baby, a baby no bigger than a thumb, Isaac Samuel all of the time. So for every day they called him

K'tonton which means very, very little; and that's exactly what he was.

The first thing she had to do was to find a cradle for the baby to sleep in.

"Fetch me the *ethrog* box," the wife said to her husband. "It was the *ethrog* that brought my precious K'tonton and the *ethrog* box shall be his cradle."

She lifted the cover of the box, a curving, rounded cover. When she turned it over it rocked gently to and fro. Then she took the flax that the *ethrog* had been wrapped in, and spun it and wove it into the softest linen. Out of the linen she made a wee coverlet and a sheet. Wherever she went and what ever she did, little K'tonton in his wee cradle went with her. When she kneaded the dough for the Sabbath, she set the cradle on the table beside her.

"It will put a blessing on the bread," she said.

Often she placed the cradle in an eastern window. "Perhaps a sunbeam from Palestine will steal down to him."

She fed him milk and honey in it—Palestine honey. "The *Torah* is like milk and honey," she said. "I will feed you milk and honey now, and when you grow older you will feed on *Torah*."

Sometimes K'tonton opened his wee mouth and cried. You would never believe so loud a sound could come from so wee a space. Then K'tonton's mother carried him, cradle and all, into the room where his father sat studying all day long in the big books of the Talmud. Back and forth K'tonton's father swayed reciting the Hebrew pages. Back and forth K'tonton rocked in his wee cradle listening to the words and thinking them the pleasantest sound he had ever heard, even pleasanter than his mother's lullabies.

So K'tonton grew until he was as tall as his father's middle finger. By this time he wasn't a baby any longer. He was three years old, and wore trousers and a little blouse and a tiny *Arba Kanforth* of finest silk. You could see the fringes of the *Arba Kanforth* sticking out from under his blouse.

Now, when K'tonton's mother was cooking and baking for the Sabbath, there was no cooing baby to watch her from his cradle. No—there was a busy little chatterbox of a K'tonton, dancing about on the table, peeping into the cinnamon box, hiding behind the sugar bowl, asking a question, so many questions, that at last his mother would say, "Blessing on your head, K'tonton, if you don't let me keep my mind on my work, I'll be putting salt in the cake and sugar in the fish." But before anything of the sort happened, K'tonton had a most exciting adventure. Only that is a story in itself.

——*Sadie Rose Weilerstein*

Kugel, a Sabbath pudding.
Torah means "the teaching" applied originally to the five books of Moses but also used to designate the entire sacred literature of the Jews.
Arba Kanforth, an inner garment with fringes on each of its four corners worn in accordance with the biblical command.

K'tonton Takes a Ride on a Runaway Trendel

IT WAS *Hanukah,* the Feast of Lights. The first little Hanukah light was shining in the window. Aunt Gittel and Uncle Israel had come to visit. So had the little old "Bobe." You remember her, don't you? The little old woman who sat next to K'tonton's mother in synagogue and told her what to do if she wanted to have a child. From the kitchen came the pleasant sizzle, sizzle of frying *latkes.* Everybody was laughing and singing and chattering, everyone but K'tonton. K'tonton sat in a corner by himself as sober as a week day. There wasn't a smile on his face, not the tiniest bit of a smile. And all because of his GREAT AMBITION. He had told the lions on the *Hanukah* lamp all about that ambition the day before.

"See my Palestine box—the blue one with the white star. I'm going to fill it to the very top. Clinkety, clink,

"K'tonton Takes a Ride on a Runaway Trendel" is from *Adventures of K'tonton,* by Sadie Rose Weilerstein; copyright, 1935, by The Women's League of the United Synagogue of America. The inclusion of this story does not indicate the endorsement by the Women's League of joint Christmas-Hanukah celebrations.

away the pennies will go to Palestine! They're to buy land, you know—for the Jewish farmers, the Haluzim. You ought to buy a big piece of land with a whole box of money."

But of course, if K'tonton wanted to fill this box, he had to have *Hanukah Gelt;* and no one in the room had offered him any, not Father, not Mother, not Bobe, not Uncle Israel or Aunt Gittel.

"Maybe they're hungry and that made them forget," thought K'tonton. "Perhaps they'll remember after they have had their *latkes*."

But no! Mother brought the *latkes* in, a great platterful for the grown-ups, a wee plateful for K'tonton. Every *latke* was eaten and still no one said a word about *Hanukah Gelt*.

"Perhaps I ought to remind them," thought K'tonton. "I'll go right up and say, 'Don't you know it's *Hanukah*? Don't you know you're supposed to give *Hanukah Gelt* on *Hanukah*?'"

But no, it wouldn't be polite to ASK for *Hanukah Gelt*.

"Come here, little sober sides," called Uncle Israel picking K'tonton up in his hand. "Where's your *Hanukah* smile? Get the *trendel,* Gittel! We've got to wake our K'tonton up."

Out came the *trendel*, the whirling Hanukah top with Hebrew letters on the sides. Uncle Israel seated K'tonton on top. Whirl! Twirl! and K'tonton and the *Hanukah trendel* were spinning about on the table. Round and round, round and round twirled the trendel. Faster and faster, faster and faster, faster and faster. Then slower, slower, slow! It swayed. It stopped. K'tonton peered over the side.

"Gimel!" he called. His cheeks were rosy with excitement. He had forgotten his disappointment or almost forgotten it.

"Your turn, Aunt Gittel!" he called.

Whirl! Twirl! the *trendel* was off again. Straight across the table it went with K'tonton on it.

"Watch out!" cried Father. "It's going over the side."

And over the side it went. Down from the table, across the floor, out through the doorway! Spin, bump! Spin, bump! Down the stairs and out into the street! Down the stairs and out into the street after the runaway *trendel* went Father! And after Father, Mother, and after Mother, Uncle Israel and Bobe and Aunt Gittel.

"Stop the *trendel*! Stop it! Stop it!" called Father to a fat policeman on the corner.

"Stop it! Stop it! Stop it!" cried Bobe and Aunt Gittel and Uncle Israel all together.

But the policeman was an Irishman and didn't know what a *trendel* was.

On and on sped the Hanukah top with K'tonton holding fast. He laughed aloud. It was so jolly an adventure. Now they were at the corner. Now they had turned the corner and were spinning on—down a dark alley, around another corner, on and on and on. And still the *trendel* spun. Would it never stop? K'tonton was not laughing now. Perhaps this was a punishment. Hadn't he sulked about the *Hanukah Gelt*? Had he not spoiled the joy of the holiday with his frown? He must accept what would befall him.

"Gam zu l'tovah," said K'tonton. "This, too, is for the best!"

As he spoke the *trendel* swerved. It turned into a gutter.

It swayed drunkenly. It stopped. K'tonton sprang to his feet and looked about. Something was shining in the darkness. It wasn't—it couldn't be—but it was! A BIG ROUND SHINING QUARTER!

Up came Father panting and out of breath. He stopped over the gutter to pick up his frightened K'tonton. But there wasn't any frightened K'tonton. There was a laughing, joyful K'tonton hugging a shining quarter to his breast.

"*Hanukah Gelt,* Father!" cried K'tonton. "For my Palestine box."

"*Hanukah Gelt?*" said Father. "If I didn't forget all about *Hanukah Gelt!*"

"*Hanukah Gelt,* Mother," cried K'tonton with a smile as broad as his face.

"*Hanukah Gelt?*" said Mother. "If I didn't forget all about *Hanukah Gelt!*"

Up came Uncle Israel and Aunt Gittel and little old Bobe.

"*Hanukah Gelt,* Uncle Israel! See my *Hanukah Gelt,* Bobe, Aunt Gittel!" And K'tonton held his precious quarter high.

"*Hanukah Gelt!*" cried Bobe and Aunt Gittel and Uncle Israel together. "To think we forgot about *Hanukah Gelt!*"

Then Father picked up his little son and carried him home, *trendel, Hanukah Gelt* and all, down the street, up the stairs into the house, straight to the big blue and white Palestine box. High up to the top of the box K'tonton was lifted—and then—and then—

Father emptied his pockets. He emptied them of every penny, and nickel, and quarter, and dime that was in them. And Uncle Israel emptied his pockets. And Mother and Aunt Gittel emptied their pocketbooks. And the little old Bobe took out her handkerchief and untied a knot in the corner of it and shook out eight shining new pennies, one for each night of the holiday. The *Hanukah Gelt* was piled up at the side of the blue box so high, it covered the star. Father handed up the coins and K'tonton rolled up his sleeves and pushed each one down the slot of the Palestine box.

"Hurrah!" cried K'tonton as the last *Hanukah* coin went clinkety, clink into the box. "Hurrah for *Hanukah Gelt*! Hurrah for *Eretz Israel*! Hurrah for the runaway *trendel*!"

——Sadie Rose Weilerstein

Trendel or dreidel, a four sided top spun on Hanukah; each side is inscribed with a Hebrew letter, *Nun Gimel He Shin* standing for *Nes Gadol Hayah Shom,* "a great miracle took place here."
Eretz Israel, the land of Israel. Palestine.

Latkes

If *Latkes* you would make
Salt and eggs and flour take—
Eat with jest and song and rhyme,
At the festive Hanukkah time.

A Hanukkah Top

Turn, my top, around, around,
Past the kish and pit and mound,
Past the vineyard, brook and rill,
Past the valley and the hill,
On to Kishon, as you veer,
When you meet a pioneer,
Tell your legend, bring him cheer:
"Miracles have happened here."

Once this land was swampy, friend,
Now to that has come an end.
Conquered were the waste and mud
In a battle void of blood;
Not with swords was won the soil,
But with ceaseless, endless toil.

Unto Modin, swiftly fly,
And your tidings shout and cry;
"Maccabeans, rest in peace
Lo, your valiant heirs increase.
In the vanguard they wage war,
Planting vineyards by the score,
Swinging hammers, hauling loads,
Building houses, paving roads . . ."

Tell your legend, bring him cheer:
"Miracles are happening here!"
——*N. D. Karpinver*

"A Hanukkah Top" is from *Gems of Hebrew Verse,* edited by Harry H. Fein; copyright 1940 by Bruce Humphries, Inc., Boston.

David Comes Home
A Hanukah Story of Today

DAVID STOOD on the deck of the ocean liner watching the passengers hurrying down the gangplank. He leaned against the ice-covered deck rail, his chin pressed hard against his skinny arms. Watching friends and families exchange greetings, he wondered who, on that crowded New York dock, was meeting him.

His Uncle Harry had sent for him. At the camp for War Orphans in Austria, people had congratulated him and envied him because he was going from the crowded, dismal shelter to the United States. He had been full of excitement then. A family, even one he didn't know, sounded wonderful. But now he was here, he wondered what his uncle would think of him. Even more important, how would his two cousins, Joseph and Anna, feel about having a ten year old boy suddenly come to live in their house?

"Well, I'll know soon enough," thought Dave, as he picked up his suitcase and made his way to the thinning line. "Anyway I'm glad I learned to speak English."

As he passed down the gangplank he heard a boy saying, "See, over there! That little blonde kid . . . he looks like the picture."

"I'm not a little kid!" said David to himself as he walked toward the boy and a tall, blonde man. "But I guess they mean me."

In a deep booming voice the man said, "Hello son, aren't you David Sherman?"

David saluted as he had been taught by the army officers in charge of the camp. "Yes sir!" he answered.

"You're out of the army, now," said Uncle Harry, and laughed a pleasant rumble. "Meet your cousin Joe. I'll get this last paper cleared. I've taken care of all the rest, so we should be out in a moment."

The boys shook hands. Although both boys were about ten years old, Joe's laughing face looked younger than David's. Joseph had curly red hair, and he was bigger and heavier than his thin blonde cousin.

"Were you really in the army?" asked Joe.

"No," answered Dave. "But we all worked against the Nazis. Because I'm blonde and small and I look German, I carried messages. The Germans didn't even stop me."

Uncle Harry came back in time to hear him. He put his arm around David's shoulder for a moment. "Everyone is in the army in a modern war," he said. "Come on boys, we have a train to catch." He explained to David, "We live a short ride out of New York City."

"This is quite a limousine," said David, as they got into a shining new taxi. "I didn't think there could be so many good cars," he added, looking out of the window.

As they rode slowly through the heavy traffic he could see into the glittering store windows decorated for the Christmas season. Food in huge pyramids, candies strewn like colored snowflakes, toys, clothing—it was a dreamland. There was one window with a team of reindeer pulling a loaded sleigh up into a starry sky. Colored boxes of every shape and size tumbled out onto the sparkling toy town.

"So much, so much of everything," whispered David.

On the street corners men in Santa Claus costumes rang bells over small open kettles. "Christmas collection," explained Joe. At Grand Central station they stepped out of the taxi right in front of one of the kettles. Uncle Harry dropped a coin into it. The Santa rang his bell and said a cheery, "Merry Christmas."

David felt a chill of fear. He forgot his shyness.

"Are Jews here *forced* to celebrate Christmas? Are you forbidden to—to—observe the holidays of your faith?"

"Listen to the fancy lingo," Joe laughed. David felt his face grow hot at the teasing note he thought he heard in his cousin's voice. "Sure we are forced to have all kinds of parties at Christmas time," said Joe. "We have to go to Christmas parties and Hanukah parties. We even have to give each other gifts. It's all very sad."

David didn't feel free to answer back. To himself he thought, "It wouldn't be so jolly to him if he'd seen gangs of German storm troopers instead of Santas on every corner."

Uncle Harry interrupted gravely. "Joe hasn't seen the things you have, David. Don't worry yourself. No one *forces* us to celebrate anything here. This week, while some of our friends and neighbors are celebrating their holiday, Christmas, we and some other neighbors are celebrating our Festival of Lights, or Hanukah. We light bright candlesticks, they put lights on trees. We all exchange presents and we have fun together. The coin I put in the kettle is for a needy person in the holiday season. A real American doesn't care what faith, just any needy person. We celebrate different holidays for different reasons, but we can all get along as neighbors and friends."

David thought, "Can I get along with these different neighbors and friends? Will I fit in?"

As they went down the huge stairway to the trains, Joe walked at Dave's side. "You know Dave, I thought I wouldn't be able to understand you and here you talk like a fancy English movie actor."

"I learned in a camp from an English nurse," said Dave quietly. Unhappily he wondered if Joe was poking fun at him.

Joseph took a chocolate bar out of his pocket and passed a big piece to Dave. They nibbled while the train pulled out of the station. Between mouthfuls Joe said, "We were surprised when we got the telegram this morning telling us your boat was arriving earlier. We thought you were coming the day after tomorrow. It's fun to arrive on a holiday. We're having a party tonight. Did you ever have any Hanukah celebrations where you were?"

His Uncle Harry answered for him. "I guess David didn't get much celebrating done, Joe. His war was a lot worse than ours."

David thought of the only Hanukah he could remember

with his parents. "I remember one," he answered. "I was about five or six years old. We were living hidden in a cellar room—a store room. There were sacks of potatoes in one corner. They smelled damp. Father cut one of the potatoes to make a candle holder. The woman who lived upstairs gave us some candles from her Christmas tree. She was helping us hide. She didn't like the Nazis either.

" 'It's a dark night for us all,' she said, when my mother thanked her.

"And my father answered, 'We'll brighten it up. You know, after the longest night the days get brighter and brighter.' "

"Why were you hiding? Did you do something wrong? Were you in enemy country?" asked Joe.

"Hasn't he heard of anything," thought David. Aloud, he answered, "We didn't do anything wrong, but we were Jews. The Nazis said that was a crime. They killed those they caught."

"Sounds real friendly," shivered Joe. "Tell me more about the Hanukah celebration."

"Mother covered the cellar window with potato sacks so no light would come through. Then we lit the candles and sang 'The Rock of Ages.' "

"That's a very old Jewish hymn," said Uncle Harry.

"Didn't you get any presents?" asked Joe.

"I got one," said Dave, "a cat, from the lady upstairs. I had it for company until we had to move on to another hiding place. Pets are fun."

"I have a dog!" said Joe.

"I've always wanted a dog," said David. He was so busy with his thoughts he didn't see the pleased smile Joe and Uncle Harry exchanged. In his mind he saw

himself walking along a country road with his parents.
They were escaping somewhere. There was a little puppy
waddling past them on short fat legs and he wanted to
take it with him.

"No time to play with dogs when your business is with
Nazi wolves." His father laughed his big friendly laugh.
"It's not safe for dogs these days."

David shifted the suitcase at his feet. He read the label.
Name—David Sherman. Address—no address. The train
lurched, jolted to a stop and Dave bumped his head on
the seat in front of him. Both boys laughed.

"Great work old boy," said Joe. "Hit it again with
your head."

Uncle Harry picked up the suitcases. "Here we are
boys."

Snow was falling. In the station square there was a big
Christmas tree shining with hundreds of bulbs.

"So many Christmas trees, here, all lit up," said Dave,
"makes me feel I'm in the wrong place."

"You don't need to feel that it is so strange, you know,"
said Uncle. "Many religions have a festival with lights
this time of year. Christmas trees, candles, lamps, fireworks, bonfires— they are all part of the winter festivals.
There are other reasons for them, too, but the longest,
blackest winter nights make everyone long for the sunlight. So, when the days begin getting longer, everyone
celebrates."

They turned in at a house with a wide porch. From
across the street, as if from behind a decorated Christmas
tree on a lawn, a voice called, "Hi, Joe."

Joe shouted back, "Hi, Mike, see you later."

In front of them a door opened. A black cocker spaniel

barked and bounded off the stairs into a snow bank. The snow came right up to the dog's nose but he puffed and heaved and threw himself at Joe.

"You don't need to go skiing Pal. I'll get to you," said Joe patting the dog. Pal licked Joe's face, whined and barked and then fell over into the snow in his excitement at having his master back. Dave reached over to pat him, but the dog growled slightly.

"He's a one man dog," said Uncle Harry, "Joe's dog."

David thought, "Even the dog thinks I shouldn't be here." Ahead, there was the sound of a girl's high, squeaky voice. "Where is he? Didn't you find him? Isn't he coming?"

And a woman's low voice whispered, "Sh, Monkey, not so loud."

For one moment David suddenly missed the camp. It was silly of him, he knew, but there the people understood each other without explanations. He felt so strange here. He wondered if he and Joe could ever be friends.

His aunt welcomed him softly. She didn't try to kiss him, just shook both his hands. His little cousin Anna jumped around him. Questions popped out of her like tracer bullets.

"Are you David? Did you really live in a war? Did you get saved from a con-concent-ration camp? Did your mother and father get killed? Is that suitcase all you brought?"

"Anna, be quiet!" said Uncle Harry. But that only tripped up her words for a moment and she rushed on. "Can you shoot a gun? Were you a spy . . . ?"

Her father picked her up, threw her over his shoulders and said, "We've things to do in the garage, for the party.

I'm sorry David, she's like a soda pop. When she starts to fizz it's hard to get the cap on again."

"Don't mind her," said Aunt Miriam. "She isn't quite seven. She thinks everything that happens is exciting, like a story book."

"She's a pest," said Joe. "Let's get ready for the party."

"Right," said Aunt Miriam. "It's getting late and we want to begin. Let's go to your room, David, and put your suitcase away and have a quick wash." She smiled at him and David tripped over the rug in his eagerness to follow her. "You're the biggest Hanukah present I've ever had," she went on. "I'm glad your boat got here today. It really makes it a party."

She opened the door of a small, pleasant room. "This is yours," said Aunt Miriam, "if you need anything."

"Just holler," said Joe as he popped his head out of a door across the hall.

Then he was alone in his room. It was something he would have to get accustomed to slowly . . . a real bed, a small soft chair, a table with white paper, a tray of pencils and crayons—a shelf under the window with some magazines and books.

The sound of Joe galloping past told him it was time to go down. He could hear his little cousin still questioning, "Is he coming down? Is he going to stay here for always?"

That was the question in his mind, too. Would they want him to stay, or were they disappointed in him? But now there was the Hanukah celebration to think about. And that would be fun.

David came down to the living room. Everyone was sitting in front of the glowing fireplace except Anna, who was teasing the dog with the end of her brown braid. On the mantle-piece were little packages tied in colored ribbons. On the sofa, on the floor, on the wide window sill, were boxes in gay wrappings. Joe and Anna were peeking at the packages.

"Wonder what this is? Golly here's a big one. Do you see anything that might be the red pocketbook I want?"

Uncle and Aunt laughed, "No peeking now, till after we light the candles."

On the window sill was a beautifully polished, shining candleholder, the special Hanukah one called a Menorah.

"Who is going to light the first candle?" piped Anna.

"Questions, and more questions," Uncle Harry pretended to sigh, "that child and her questions. What do you think, Mother?"

"You asked a question yourself!" laughed Joe.

"The first light is very important," said mother. "It means Light after Darkness. It tells of the brave Jewish soldiers who fought to bring back the light of freedom to their people. It means Light you can put in the window without fear. I think Dave should light the first candle on his first day in the United States."

"I don't remember the prayer," whispered Dave. "I haven't heard it in a long time."

"That's all right," said Uncle Harry, "we'll say it together."

"Blessed art Thou, O Lord our God . . . who has commanded us to kindle the lights of Hanukah. Blessed art Thou—who has wrought Miracles for our fathers in the days of old at this season."

David lit the orange candles.

"Who will tell the story? What's the miracle?" asked Anna.

"I'll tell it too fast," said Joe winking at the gifts.

Uncle Harry began:

"A long time ago a king of Syria tried to make the Jews give up their beliefs. In those days a country had to take the religion of the ruler. He ordered them to put statues of the Green Gods into their temples and to pray to these idols. But the Jews were not like the other con-quered people. They refused to obey the king. He sent soldiers who tried to terrify the people by killing many men, women and children. But if the wicked king thought force would change their beliefs, he was mistaken. The people fought back."

"He's like my father," thought Dave. "He'd fight back, he'd never give in."

"Groups of people got together—even children helped." He smiled at David. "Just like David's friends in the war just past. Guerilla bands got together. They formed an army. Judah Maccabeus and his brothers had seen their father killed. They led the army. It wasn't grand and well-fed and well-equipped like the Syrian king's army of paid soldiers. But they had heart for the battle—they had faith and courage. And the little army of honest men beat the king's army."

"Men who would rather fight and die than surrender and live," said mother, "cannot be conquered." She looked at David, "David's father was like that."

"George Washington was something like Judah Macca-beus, wasn't he?" asked Joe.

"Yes," answered Uncle, "a small American army beat a

great Empire. Perhaps it was because they fought for the right to be free people."

"But what about the candles and the Menorah? Why do we light them?" asked Anna.

"Well, after the battle, the happy soldiers went right to the temple to light the holy lamp. The Greeks had left it dirty. Broken statues lay all about. Animals had lived there. The holy lamp which should always be burning, went out. Quickly the men scrubbed and cleaned the temple. The priests came to bless the place again. But they could find only one bottle of pure, clean oil still sealed tightly. There seemed hardly enough for one night. But the men didn't want to wait. 'Better light for a while,' they agreed, 'than none at all until the messengers come back.'

"But when they had put all the oil they had into the great lamp, a wonderful thing happened. The lights did not go out. They burned for eight days and eight nights, brighter and brighter. By that time the messengers had come back from another city with fresh, clean oil.

"That is why," continued Uncle, "we light the candles for eight days, one more each day so that they too burn brighter and brighter. The ninth candle is used to light the others. We celebrate the lights that endured and grew brighter. But we honor even more the faith and courage of the brave men who fought one of the first battles to show that people will never, never give up their freedom."

"And people of every faith have done such fighting," added mother.

"And now," said Uncle Harry.

"The presents!" shouted Joe and Anna.

With a wild Indian whoop Joe leaped up. Aunt Miriam

patted the seat next to herself on the sofa. "Sit by me, Dave," she said. "Stay safe while these Indians cover us in paper and string."

There was a quietness and gentleness that came out of Aunt Miriam. She was small, but she wasn't lost, as he was, in Joe's noisy feet and quick humor, in Anna's firecracker questions. She belonged, like a mast in a boat. He felt like something tossed up on deck.

First Joe and Anna went at the gifts piled around the Menorah. There were little packages for everyone. Colored balls, little paper candy boxes like houses, small games, chocolates, tangerines, blue paper horns, puzzles and blue and white balloons.

Everyone blew up the balloons which went bouncing around the room. The dog, Pal, was chasing them. Just as his paw hit one of them, the balloon bounded quietly away. Pal was stalking it, making small ferocious growls. He was so jolly and funny Dave tried to pat him, but the dog returned no friendly sign.

"Don't fret, Dave," said Uncle Harry. "He's just barely polite to the rest of us. He's just Joe's dog."

"That's the way a dog should be," said Dave trying not to sound hurt as he was.

The sound of tearing paper was all around the room. Anna opened a box and cooed at the shiny little sewing machine. "Did you ever see such a darling? Can it sew?" and without waiting for an answer she went on tearing open the boxes. There were pretty clothes for her and for her doll. There were pieces of cloth to sew things on the new machine. There were bright warm things— a red hat, scarf and mitten set. David sat dazed by the display.

Joe went at things just a little more slowly. He patted his beautiful tool chest, with the gleaming steel tools neatly stowed in the light-colored wood chest. Dave wondered if Joe would ever let him use them.

"I guess these will be just Joe's tools, like Joe's dog," he thought.

There were books for Joe, a photograph album and a kit for building an old-fashioned trolley car. A big white sweater with heavy waterproof gloves and a ski cap came out of one box. "Bring on the dog-sled," shouted Joe as he pranced around in the gloves and cap.

"Here's the dog-sled," said Uncle Harry as he came in from the hall pulling a long toboggan sled. "This is the family present."

Joe and Anna jumped on while Uncle pretended to pull. Pal jumped through the crackling papers and landed on Joe's lap with a red ribbon caught on one ear. "We're off," they shouted.

Anna tumbled into a pile of colored wrapping paper and lay there laughing. Suddenly she squealed and pointed upward. Hanging from the light was a red pocket-book. Uncle Harry put Anna up on his shoulders to reach it.

"Joe did that," said Aunt Miriam, "he loves to give surprises."

"Oh, I'm so happy, so happy," said Anna hugging the red pocketbook.

"The child is ill," laughed mother, "she said something that wasn't a question."

"They all have so much," Dave thought. It seemed as if he were still riding in the taxi looking in at windows where nothing belonged to him. He blinked and cleared his throat. He wasn't going to show how he felt at not having any big, important boxes marked "David." They had tried, and he *had* come early. There were the little fun things, and a sweater, a pad of drawing paper, some mittens. He shouldn't feel jealous but he couldn't keep his eyes off the others' pile of gifts.

"We left getting you sport things until we saw you, Dave, for size," said his aunt. He was embarrassed that his face showed his feelings.

"You don't need to buy me presents," he said quickly. "I'm too big for that."

"Well, listen to that," teased Joe. "He's too big for presents."

"It sounded silly and conceited the way Joe said it," thought Dave. "As if I didn't want any presents."

"Doesn't Dave want his presents?" giggled Anna as she bounced a big colored ball all around the sofa. He wished they'd stop picking on him. If Anna was going to join with Joe, and make him feel foolish everytime he opened his mouth, it would be no fun.

"Of course he wants presents," said Aunt Miriam, "and he'll get them."

The children whispered together and giggled, which made Dave feel more and more like punching them.

"Before there is any more talk of presents, clear some of this paper off the floor. The McCarthy children will be here soon," said Aunt Miriam. She peered out the window. "My, their tree looks pretty with the lights on and the snow falling. Here are Mike and Marge coming across now. I'll start the pancake batter."

Mike and Marge blew in on a blast of cool air and fresh light snow. Mike had red hair and freckles, and

Marge was a pretty girl with straight black hair and bangs. She was about nine.

"Some people are lucky," she said as she met Dave. "When we get an addition to the family, all he can do is lie in a carriage and scream and sleep. Now *you* are a useful size."

"Yes," said Mike, "what we need on this street is an extra hand for stick ball. You look like you can catch."

Mike and Marge unwrapped a big cake their mother had baked. They handed it to Uncle Harry. "Here's your favorite cake—maple walnut layer," said Marge. "Mother says eat it one piece at a time."

Aunt Miriam called from the dining room, "Come on, everybody. We're starved. Let's have supper."

The table was covered with a pale blue cloth. In the center was a large star formed of gold flowers. Shining candlesticks with blue and white candles burned softly. At each place were blue and white snappers, blue paper hats, and napkins with blue and white stars.

"How pretty," said Marge. "Your blue and white Hanukah colors are like clouds and sky."

On a smaller table was a wide electric griddle. Aunt Miriam began at once to make tiny, fluffy pancakes. "We always eat pancakes on this holiday," he said. "It's an old custom."

"Do you suppose it's because you can keep right on making them and eating them while people come in and out with presents?" asked Joe.

"That's as good a reason as any," said Mike, "as long as you get pancakes. It's like Christmas plum pudding and Thanksgiving turkey."

"Yum-yum—look what goes with the pancakes," said Marge.

There was the biggest tray Dave had ever seen, filled with dishes of delicacies; honey, fluffy mounds of cream, whole red cherry jam, chopped nuts, crushed pineapple, cinnamon and sugar, apple-sauce, whipped cream cheese, pitchers of syrup.

"All or any go with the pancakes," said Aunt Miriam popping the first crisp pancakes onto plates and passing them along. Uncle Harry was done before the others and went around the room strumming a guitar. "I'll warm up for my evening's concert work," he strummed, "while you people get your nourishment."

They ate and ate. At last milk, chocolate, cookies and fruits were put on the table with the maple walnut cake. "If you can't eat any more now," said Uncle Harry, "don't worry. It will be here later, too. Let's sing now. I'll play the Hanukah Song for you. Come on—

'Oh Hanukah, O Hanukah
Come light the Menorah!
Let's have a party,
We'll all dance the horah!' "

While they were all singing a car drove into the driveway. Joe left the room, went out the door, and then as the car drove away, David could hear him going up the stairs. In a little while he came back into the room, and with a pleased smile, nodded to his mother. "Ready," his lips formed.

Aunt Miriam got up from the table, "Now before we have games and music, and before more neighbors come in, let's get our presents out of the way."

David tried hard. But he couldn't help feeling jealous as he picked up the few things that were his. It was silly to be angry when he had received more gifts than he could remember. But the other children each had something special and important all their own. Aunt Miriam would take him shopping for clothes the next day, but it wasn't the same party feeling.

He went upstairs to his room, Joe and Anna following with their many gifts. There were so many, Mike and Marge were helping them carry their things. They all stopped outside his door, as if waiting for something. He opened the door and started to step in. What was that, there on the floor? He blinked hard. But it stayed.

There, in a wicker bed, on a bright plaid pillow, was a puppy—and such a puppy!

The noise of the door had startled it, and David and the dog stared at each other with bright, surprised eyes. It was a light golden cocker spaniel, and as it rubbed its beady black nose with a paw, the long ears fell right over its little face.

"Isn't he an angel?" said Anna breaking the silence.

"Happy Hanukah, happy Hanukah," called the children.

The dog was a little frightened. He whimpered and David picked him up ever so gently. The dog snuggled in his arms. It put out a tongue as pink as a petal and licked David's face. Then, worn out with that hard work, it dropped its head into the crook of David's arm and fell asleep. David stroked the little warm head.

He saw the leash, the gay plaid bed. He heard Joe say, "Sorry we were late. The kennel man couldn't get 'down early enough after the change in boat time. He just came."

Anna gave him a ball and a rubber bone. "Joe even got a tag. We didn't forget anything, did we?"

Joe and he smiled at each other. Joe had planned it all. Joe was all right! Now he was saying to the others, "Come on out gang, let them alone for a while. The dog has to get to know his master."

They left David with his puppy. He could hear them tossing the boxes into their rooms, then the rush of feet past his door and down the stairs to the living room. Then Anna was saying, "Isn't he coming down?"

And Joe's voice, not mean or nasty, just with a jolly note of teasing, "Take your time, small fry, he's here to stay."

David reached for the tag at the dog's throat. He read it quickly and then slowly again.

Owner's name: David Sherman
Home address: 14 Pine Road, West Town,
    New York

He hugged the puppy, "See that, puppy! We have a home!"

——Nina Schneider

A Song of Always

The Temple is clean
   The lamp burns bright;
Judah the leader,
   Has started the light.

The sun shines by day,
   And dark is the night;
But always and always
   The lamp burns bright.
      ——*Efraim Rosenzweig*

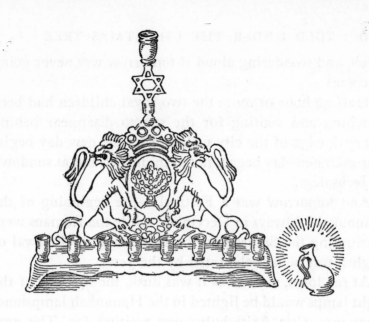

The Festival of Lights
43 B.C.

OVER THE TEMPLE and the housetops of Jerusalem, over its smoking altar, and its Mount of Zion, a red winter sun was slowly sinking. Much too slowly, it seemed to the two children who were watching it that December afternoon from the palace of their grandfather, the High Priest, Hyrcanus.

Marianne, a very beautiful little girl of eleven or twelve, stood quietly leaning against the window frame, her long lashes and heavy dark curls turned to red bronze in the sunlight.

Aristobulus, who was nine and more impatient than his sister, kept turning in his hands a small unlighted

"The Festival of Lights" is from *Augustus Caesar's World,* by Genevieve Foster; copyright, 1947, by Genevieve Foster; this selection reprinted by permission of Charles Scribner's Sons.

torch, and wondering aloud if tomorrow was never going to come!

Half an hour or more the two royal children had been watching and waiting for the sun to disappear behind the dark edge of the city wall and let the new day begin. For each new day began, not at midnight, but at sundown in Jerusalem.

And tomorrow was a Festival!—the beginning of the Hannukah! Always in December, while the Romans were celebrating the Saturnalia, the Hannukah, or Festival of Lights, was being celebrated by the Jews.

At sundown, as soon as it was dusk, the first one of the eight lamps would be lighted in the Hannukah lampstand. That was what Aristobulus was waiting for. The next evening, they would light two lamps instead of one. The next three, and so on, until on the last day, all of the eight branches of the Hannukah lampstand would be ablaze with light. Lights would be shining out from all the houses in Jerusalem.

The sacred gold lampstand in the Temple had only seven branches, like the seven days of the week, or the seven planets in the sky. But the Hannukah lampstand had eight lamps, in memory of the miracle.

According to a legend, which Marianne and Aristobulus never tired of hearing repeated, a miracle had taken place in the Temple in the days of one of their early ancestors, Judas Maccabeus. It had been on a December day about one hundred years ago, when the Greeks instead of the Romans had ruled over Palestine.

The Temple, after being long misused by the Greeks for the worship of one of their many Gods, had just been won back again by the Jews and was about to be rededi-

cated to Javeh, the one and only God of Israel. Everything was ready. The altar had been cleansed and purified.
New golden basins had been provided to catch the blood
of the lambs, waiting to be sacrificed. The twelve loaves
of unleavened bread had been laid on the table in the
Holy Place. And there, too, once more, standing like
the tree of life, was the great sacred lamp, or candlestick,
with its seven branches. It had only to be filled and
lighted.

Then, to the dismay of the priests, no pure lamp oil
could be found. A frantic search unearthed but one small
dusty jar, containing only enough sacred oil to last a single
day, but with it the seven cups were filled and lighted.
The next day, to the amazement of the priests, it was still
burning, and the next. For eight days, it was said, the
oil continued to burn. In joy, then and thanksgiving, Judas
Maccabeus had decreed, that every year for eight days,
the miracle should be commemorated with a solemn
festival of joy and thanksgiving.

For eight days, therefore, this year, as every year, while
the Hannukah lights were burning, the Temple walls
would resound with the singing of psalms, and their chorus
of Hallel-u-jah, or "Praise-to-Javeh," God of Israel.

Judas Maccabeus was the great hero who had defeated
the Greeks and won back the Temple. He was an ancestor
in whom the two royal children felt great pride, though
just how they were related to him Aristobulus never could
remember.

He knew only that they, too, were Maccabeans, and
that since the days of Maccabeus, all the High Priests had
belonged to the Maccabean family.

"Judas Maccabeus," Marianne explained to him again,

"had four brothers. One of them was the great-great-grandfather of our grandfather Hyrcanus."

"And all those grandfathers have been High Priests," said Aristobulus. "Some day, do you think there may be another High Priest strong enough to fight and drive the Romans out, the same way Judas Maccabeus drove away the Greeks? Judas Maccabeus . . ." he said thoughtfully. "I can spell that name."

Diverted for a moment from his vigil, the boy laid down the small torch, and slowly traced the name of his brave ancestor in Hebrew characters on the dusty window sill.

Then he looked up, and saw that suddenly, while he wasn't watching, the sun had dropped below the western horizon, and it was tomorrow! It was Hannukah. The first day of the Festival of Lights.

————*Genevieve Foster*

Javeh, the Hebrew name for God.

Blessings for Chanukah

Blessed art Thou, O God our Lord,
Who made us holy with his word,
And told us on this feast of light
To light one candle more each night.

(Because when foes about us pressed
   To crush us all with death or shame,
The Lord his priests with courage blest
To strike and give his people rest
And in the House that he loved best
   Relight our everlasting flame.)

Blest art Thou, the whole world's King,
Who did so wonderful a thing
For our own fathers true and gold
At this same time in days of old!
      ——*Jessie E. Sampter*

"Blessings for Chanukah" is from *Around the World in Rhymes for the Jewish Child*, by Jessie E. Sampter; copyright, 1920, by the Bloch Publishing Company; reprinted by permission.

The Cruse of Oil
165 B.C.

LITTLE BENJAMIN shifted from one brown foot
to the other, for he was very tired. It seemed to the six-
year old boy that he had stood for hours beside his grandfather, waiting in the outer court of the Temple for Judas,
the Maccabee, and his victorious army to enter Jerusalem
in triumph. There were very few young men among the
throng which crowded to greet the conquerer; they had
been away at the war with Judas and his lion-hearted
brothers. But the women and children whom they had
fought to save from the cruel oppression of the Syrian
tyrant, Antiochus, had gathered to greet their heroes with
palms and gay garlands in their hands. There were many
gray-bearded men also, too old for fighting, who this day
praised God that they had lived long enough to see the
Temple of their fathers rescued from the defiling hands
of the Syrian oppressors.

"The Cruse of Oil" is from *Tales Old and New,* by Elma Erlich Levinger;
copyright, 1926, by the Bloch Publishing Company; reprinted by permission.

Benjamin's grandfather, Aaron ben Abraham, was among them, a stern old man, grown harsh and bitter since the death of his only son, Benjamin's father, on the battle-field. Benjamin's mother had died shortly afterwards, leaving Benjamin in the care of the silent old man, whose heart was well-nigh broken over his two griefs, the loss of his son, the enslavement of his country. Even today, when all the land of Israel rejoiced and thanked God for deliverance, Aaron ben Abraham stood with gloomy face, silent amid the shouting.

Timidly Benjamin pulled at his hand. "Grandfather," he whispered. "May I join David and Elias and the others?" He pointed to the group of boys his own age, laughing happily together. "When Judas comes they plan to run out and throw their fairest flowers before him. May I be with them?"

His grandfather frowned. "Nay. They are rough and noisy. We at least will be silent and devout in the midst of all this loud rejoicing."

The boy looked up at him with astonished eyes. "But, Grandfather, shouldn't we rejoice today because we are free, because Judas Maccabeus has driven the Syrians away and we can cleanse the Temple and make it holy once more?"

"No!" The old man's voice was harsh and bitter. "To-day we should think of those whose blood has bought us peace. Today we should offer solemn sacrifices to the God of our fathers, praying Him to keep our feet in His path of righteousness, lest we go easily astray and He punish us for our sins as He did beneath the rod of Antiochus. And children," here he frowned toward the group of merry boys, "children, above all others, should be silent before their elders. The more you make your books your companions and shun these idle, noisy fellows, the better."

He spoke more sternly, perhaps, than he intended; Benjamin's face flushed at the note of angry reproof in his voice. His lips trembled and his eyes filled with tears.

His grandfather shook him angrily. "I am ashamed of you," he said. "At a word you tremble and weep like a girl. Leave me before you put me to shame before your friends. When you can act like a man, then you may return and stand by my side again."

Hurt and humiliated, little Benjamin slunk away, ashamed to meet the eyes of those about him who heard his grandfather's rebuke. The other boys in the crowd waited to greet their fathers; at least, they clung to their mother's hands and knew they were not alone in the world. But Benjamin felt that he had not a single friend.

With lagging feet he passed into one of the smaller rooms of the long-deserted Temple. He shivered with disgust at what he saw there, the altar, on which it was rumored swine's flesh had been offered, lay broken and battered; the floor was strewn with refuse and with the soiled garments of the Syrian soldiers who had reveled there before Judas and his warriors had driven them from Jerusalem. It seemed to him that the Temple would never be made clean and beautiful again. Bursting into tears, he threw himself down upon the ground, his head pillowed on his arms. There he lay, sobbing with all his might, until at last his tired body relaxed and he fell asleep.

Benjamin was awakened by a great blaring of trumpets, a mighty shouting. He sat up and rubbed his eyes. So Judas had entered the Temple courts with his army and he had not been there to greet him. He rose unsteadily to his feet, longing to join his grandfather, yet trembling at the thought of further rebuke for his long absence.

As he lagged across the dirty floor, his eye caught the glimmer of an object still wonderfully bright in the neglected spot. Bending, he picked up a flask of burnished metal tightly sealed. Thrusting it in his girdle, he went slowly out to meet his grandfather.

But the dreaded scolding never came. For Aaron ben Abraham was too bowed down with his new disappointment to remember his troublesome grandson. "Alas," Benjamin heard him murmur as he found him at last among the crowd, "Alas, it is to remind us of our past sins, even as I have said. The Temple is ours again, but the Lord will permit no rejoicing, no Feast of Dedication lest we forget Him in our pride."

"Yes, the Menorah must remain unlit," nodded another patriarch mournfully. "It will take ten days at least for the swiftest messengers to bring oil to fill the lamps."

"Grandfather," said Benjamin, understanding nothing of the old man's disappointment, "See what I have found." And he drew the little cruse from his girdle.

Aaron's eyes sparkled with strange joy. "A cruse of oil for the Temple lamps!" he almost shouted, his feeble old voice quavering with joy, "and still sealed!"

"Then it has not been polluted by the heathen who defiled all the oil for the sacred lamps!" cried out a young priest, reaching out his hand for the cruse.

Others took up the cry. "Oil—oil for the lamps! We can light the Menorah today, for this oil is still sealed and fit for the sacred lights."

His wrinkled face glowing with joy, Aaron ben Abraham drew his little grandson by the hand until the two stood before Judas himself, Judas the Hammerer, with his chosen warriors around him. Although he lived to be a very old man Benjamin never forgot the broad shoulders in their shining armor, the piercing eyes and the gentle mouth.

"See!" panted Aaron in his excitement, "See what the child has found. Now we can light the lamps and rededicate our Temple to the Lord of Hosts."

Judas smiled. "He has shown us His way through the hand of a child," he said, and placed a kindly arm around Benjamin, drawing him to his side. But the child shrank back. It was all too much of a dream—to be praised instead of scolded by his grandfather, to be embraced by Judas before the cheering throng of people.

"You are not afraid of me?" asked the general.

Benjamin shook his head. "My father was one of your soldiers," he answered. "I will be one, too, when I am a man."

The great soldier looked sad. Perhaps he was tired of the long years of warfare. "The God of our fathers grant that when you are grown a man there will be peace in the land and no need for soldiers," he said. Then he smiled again and raised the boy to his shoulder that all might see the cruse the boy held in his hand.

"Into the Temple to give thanks to God!" commanded Judas the Maccabee. "With this oil the priests will light the sacred light and perchance when it is gone, He will, in His grace, replace it."

And it was so. The cruse which Benjamin was found was very small and contained so little oil that it was thought the great Menorah on the newly sanctified altar would burn one day only. But those who tell the story relate that the flame burned steadily for eight days until the messengers returned to Jerusalem with fresh oil. Thus, they add, arose a custom of burning the tapers for eight days at the Chanukah in memory of the cruse of oil which little Benjamin found in the Temple.

——*Elma Erlich Levinger*

The Feast of Lights

Kindle the taper like the steadfast star
Ablaze of evening's fore o'er the earth,
And add each night a lustre till afar
An eightfold splendor shine above thy hearth.

——Emma Lazarus

Reprinted by permission of Houghton Mifflin Company.

TOLD UNDER THE CHRISTMAS TREE

Compiled by the Literature Committee

of the

ASSOCIATION FOR CHILDHOOD EDUCATION *

MABEL ALSTETTER, *Associate Professor of Education, Miami University, Oxford, Ohio*

MAY HILL ARBUTHNOT, *Associate Professor, Western Reserve University, Cleveland, Ohio*

LELAND B. JACOBS, *Assistant Professor of Education, Ohio State University, Columbus, Ohio*

ROSEMARY E. LIVSEY, *Teacher's and Children's Department, Los Angeles Public Library, Los Angeles, California*

KATHERINE M. REEVES, *Associate Professor of Child Development, Cornell University, Ithaca, New York*

MARTHA SEELING, *Wheelock College, Boston, Massachusetts*

JENNIE WAHLERT, *Principal Jackson School, St. Louis, Missouri*

MARY LINCOLN MORSE, *Chairman*

* The Association for Childhood Education became The Association for Childhood Education International in 1946.

BY WAY OF EXPLANATION

Told Under the Christmas Tree is another book finding its place among the collections we have come to call the "Umbrella" books. Twenty years ago the Literature Committee of the Association for Childhood Education published a volume of much loved folk and fairy tales in well told versions that could be used directly with children. Its title was taken from Hans Christian Andersen's story of Olé Luköié, The Dustman. Olé comes to boys and girls at night, breathes softly upon their necks until they are quiet and ready for a story, opens up his green umbrella, finds a loved tale for all good boys and girls and passes all others by. Hence our initial book bore the title *Told Under the Green Umbrella*. Next, in an era when we were seeking stories to balance the fairy tale and to nourish the interest of the child who is realistically minded, *Told Under the Blue Umbrella*—a compilation of real and nearly real stories—was launched. With both folk or fairy and realistic stories available in collections of ours it seemed inevitable that an anthology of verse should be added and *Sung Under the Silver Umbrella* resulted. Shortly afterward a collection of modern stories in the field of fancy invited our committee to publish *Told Under the Magic Umbrella*. By this time the sub-title an "Umbrella" book was so firmly established that it was ready to take under its cover any anthology compiled by our Committee for boys and girls from the Nursery School on up and into Elementary School age.

Quite unlike its predecessors, our next Committee venture in the field of publication was made up of stories about children living in America but carrying on in their homes interesting customs and traditions growing out of their nationality, race, or religious backgrounds. A heart-warming collection of stories called *Told Under the Stars and Stripes* followed.

Each book our Literature Committee has compiled, we, its members, have thought to be our last—when appeals have come for still another. Parents have joined teachers in requests for what, to each one, was a desired collection not yet available. One out of several of our latest petitions was for an "Umbrella" book concerned with both stories and poems of the Christmas season. When, to these, was added the suggestion that we also include a group of stories and poems related to the Jewish Festival of Lights, *Told Under the Christmas Tree* came into being.

Stories and poems concerning Christmas are legion. The inception of Christmas in the birth of Christ; its Santa Claus, symbol of the spirit of giving; its tree, an evergreen, and its many variations in traditions growing up in and carried on in different countries—furnish a fertile field in which beloved stories and poems are born and nourished. Their beauty is unequaled anywhere.

Suggestions of stories and poems—favorites of boys and girls—came easily, until out of their accumulation each one was weighed; and by a majority vote of a seasoned children's Literature Committee it found its place in *Told Under the Christmas Tree*. Stories and poems that defy placing in time, definite space, or possible actuality make up a group under "In the Week When Christmas Comes"; while under "Everywhere, Everywhere, Christmas Tonight" are to be found stories and poems suggesting the universality of Christmas celebrations with their variations in customs and traditions—as each comes from a country with its own distinct celebrations. Some of the stories we had hoped to include could not be released while, within our Committee, we found we wanted to include some previously published in a preceding "Umbrella" book. Lest you, our readers, miss and want these, we are listing each with its source book.

TOLD UNDER THE GREEN UMBRELLA

"Wee Robin's Christmas Day"	Folk Tale
"Fulfilled"	Folk Tale
"The First Christmas"	Luke 11; 1–20
	Matthew 11; 1–11

TOLD UNDER THE BLUE UMBRELLA

"The Little Blue Dishes"	Author Unknown

SUNG UNDER THE SILVER UMBRELLA

"Cradle Hymn"	Martin Luther
"A Christmas Folk Song"	Lizette Woodworth Reese
"In the Bleak Mid Winter"	Christina Rossetti
"Christmas Morning"	Elizabeth Madox Roberts
"The Waits"	M. Nightingale
"A Christmas Prayer"	George Macdonald
"Ex Ore Infantium"	Frances Thompson
"Earth and Sky"	Eleanor Farjeon
"Now Every Child"	Gilbert K. Chesterton

TOLD UNDER THE MAGIC UMBRELLA

"A Happy Christmas Tree"	Frances Anne Brown
"The Gold Fish"	Julian Street

TOLD UNDER THE STARS AND STRIPES

"Maminka's Children"	Elizabeth Orton Jones
"A Piñata for Pepita"	Delia Goetz
"The Ice Skates"	Mildred Jordan
"Our Lady of Mercy"	Louis Zara
"Merry Christmas in Dakota"	Marian and Walter Havighurst

That our Committee should add to Christmas stories and poems those of the Festival of Lights is an outgrowth of the need for both Christian and Jews in a community to interpret the festival of each to the other. These stories often show the Jew sharing the festival that is so much his, or both interpreting together through story, song, tableaux, and pageantry the deeply reverent and happy hearted phases of the two festivals.

Recently we have been hearing that not only schools and non-denominational community centers but Christian organizations like our "Y's" and church groups, where only one of the festivals is inherent, are, for a better understanding in human relationships, interpreting the meaning and essence of the Feast of Lights. Coming, as they do, at the turn of the year, when the sun tarries longer and the nights grow shorter, each suggests the promise of spring and the reawakening of light in both the natural and the spiritual world.

There are many parallels between the two festivals. Both of them are founded in religious significance; the one, in the birth of Christ with its message of peace and good will; the other in the miracle of the sacred cruse of oil, supply for one day only, which burned for the eight days needed for Judas Maccabeus and his band of soldiers to restore the holy Temple held and defiled by their Syrian oppressors.

Again to the Jewish child there is no happier festival than that of Hanukkah nor is there any more joyous than Christmas to the Christian. Both festivals are made merry with feasting and gift-giving. Each one represents homecomings and wide-spread gatherings of family and friends. Both, too, reach back in the ages; the one to 165 B.C.;

the other to the beginning of the Christian era. In each there is deep significance as to what they symbolize to the human spirit. To recognize them in the intercultural life of America is to pay a tribute to the individual dignity of man, to honor his freedom to worship as he sees fit, and to respect his devotion to the symbols on which his spirit has been nourished.

Beside the common prophecy of renewed light and life in the world, and the happiness of the two festivals, there is a kinship between Hanukkah and our Thanksgiving— in both of which lie implicit the ends to which man will go to worship as he will. The Pilgrims took a daring voyage to a new and challenging land: in their holy city the Israelites, a small band of untrained men, overcame a mighty army of trained soldiers. In either case freedom for worship resulted.

The Jewish festival, like our Easter, varies in date. It is ushered in on the twenty-fifth day of the Jewish month Kislev, sometimes nearer and sometimes farther from the fixed date of Christmas, December twenty-fifth.

Today, freedom to worship again in a homeland of their own, fought for three times since it was won two thousand years ago, is uppermost in the heart of many a Jew. Again he is fighting to re-establish Israel, the land of his forefathers. To him, his Festival of Lights must take on additional significance.

For lists of the stories and poems concerning the Festival of Lights available in books already published or in periodicals, the Literature Committee gratefully acknowledges the courteous help of Phillip Goodman, Director of the Jewish Book Council; of Fannie Goldstein, also of the Book Council and the Public Library System of the

2

City of Boston; of Emmanuel Gamoran, Educational Director of the Commission on Jewish Education under the American Hebrew Congregations. It has appreciated the privilege of a conference with Rabbi Louis Binstock of Chicago's Temple Sholom and the suggestions of Sadie Rose Weilerstein. In the hope of depicting typical phases of the Festival of Lights both in its early history and as of today, the stories and poems under "Kindle the Taper Like the Steadfast Star" were selected.

Together with stories and poems of the Festival of Lights, the two Christmas groups in *Told Under the Christmas Tree,* and adding those included in our other "Umbrella" books, we, the Literature Committee of the Association for Childhood Education, offer you a goodly fare in stories and poems. These stories and poems invite a brotherly understanding in human relationships, a recognition of significant religious symbols and backgrounds, and reach deep down in the reverent or happy hearted moods of the two festivals celebrated so closely in time at the turn of the year.

We appreciate the privilege of securing Ruth Sawyer as our Foreword writer to *Told Under the Christmas Tree* and think ourselves fortunate also to have as its illustrators, Maud and Miska Petersham.

MARY LINCOLN MORSE, *Chairman Literature Committee*

1948